Professional Pilot's Study Guide
Volume 3

Propellers

Professional Pilot's Study Guide Volume 3

Propellers

Mike Burton

Airlife
England

Copyright © 1991 Mike Burton

First published in the UK in 1992
by Airlife Publishing Ltd

British Library Cataloguing in Publication Data
A catalogue record of this book is available from the British Library

ISBN 1 85310 275 X

Printed in England by Livesey Ltd, Shrewsbury SY3 9EB

Airlife Publishing Ltd

101 Longden Road, Shrewsbury SY3 9EB

Contents

1

BASIC PRINCIPLES OF PROPELLERS

1.1 Introduction

The propeller is a means of converting the power developed by the aircraft's engine into a propulsive force. A rotating propeller imparts a rearward motion to a mass of air, and the reaction to this is a forward force on the propeller blades.

The basic cross-sectional shape of the propeller blade is that of an aerofoil similar to the wing or other such lift generating surface. The propeller is driven by the aircraft's engine, either directly from the crankshaft, or via a gearbox which will usually reduce the r.p.m. of the propeller in relation to the engine r.p.m.

With the aircraft's engine running, when the propeller blade moves through the air, forces are generated, which are known as thrust and torque, and which may be regarded as near equivalents to the forces produced by a wing of lift and drag.

Thrust is the propulsive force, and torque the resistance to rotation or propeller load. The magnitude of the thrust and torque produced will be dependent upon the size, shape and number of blades, the blade angle, speed of rotation of the propeller, the air density, and the forward speed.

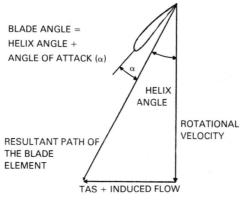

BLADE ANGLE =
HELIX ANGLE +
ANGLE OF ATTACK (α)

HELIX ANGLE

ROTATIONAL VELOCITY

RESULTANT PATH OF THE BLADE ELEMENT

TAS + INDUCED FLOW

Fig.1-1. Resultant motion and angle of attack.

1

1.2 Blade Terminology

As each blade is basically of aerofoil cross-section, thrust will be produced most efficiently at a particular angle of attack, the angle of attack being the angle between the chord line of the propeller blade at a particular blade section, or position along the blade, and the relative airflow. Fig.1-1 shows the angle of attack.

The angle of attack will vary both with operating conditions and with the camber of the blade section, however, for a given blade and given in-flight conditions, it will be relatively constant along the blade length. The rotational speed of a particular cross-section of the blade will increase the further it is from the root end of the blade and the axis of rotation, that is, the centre of the drive shaft of the propeller assembly, and as the forward speed of all parts of the blade is the same the relative airflow will vary along the length of the blade, and it is therefore necessary to decrease the blade angle from blade root to tip to generate balanced thrust conditions. Fig.1-2 shows the basic angles and twisting moments of the propeller blade.

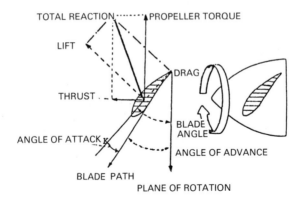

Fig.1-2. Resolution of forces.

1.3 Geometric Pitch

The geometric pitch of a propeller is the distance which it should move forward in one revolution without slip, much like a screw thread and how far it will move into its hole in one revolution. The air, however, is not solid and the propeller does not achieve its geometric pitch as a certain amount of slip will occur. Geometric pitch without slip is theoretically equal to $2\pi r \tan \Theta$, where r is the radius, or station, of a particular cross-section, and Θ is the blade angle at that point. Fixed pitch propellers are usually classified by their diameter and pitch, being related to

2

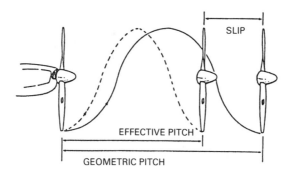

Fig.1-3. Propeller slip.

the blade angle at three-quarter radius, or other nominated station. See Fig.1-3.

1.4 Forces on a Propeller

The construction of a propeller has to be very strong in order for it to resist the various forces which act upon it during the course of its normal operation. It must also be manufactured using methods and materials which will resist the affects of the elements to which it is constantly exposed, in particular moisture and constant changes of temperature. Erosion due to dust particles in the atmosphere is also a problem, and must be considered.

The forces acting on the propeller are centrifugal, bending and twisting.

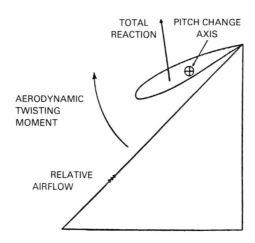

Fig.1-4. Aerodynamic twisting moment.

(a) Centrifugal Forces

Centrifugal forces will cause radial stress in the blades and the blade or propeller hub, and when acting on the material which is not on the axis of the blade will cause a twisting moment. This can be seen in Fig.1-4.

Centrifugal force on a propeller can be divided into two components within the plane of rotation. The first is the radial force parallel to the blade axis, and the other is a force at 90 degrees to the blade axis.

The radial component, or force parallel to the blade axis, produces radial stress, whilst the force at 90 degrees to the blade axis will tend to turn the blade to a finer pitch by creating a twisting action.

This turning effect is the centrifugal twisting moment and is shown in Fig.1-5.

It should be noted: the wider the blade, the greater the twisting moment.

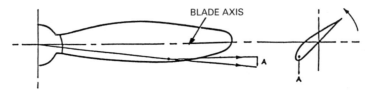

BLADE AXIS

Fig.1-5. Centrifugal twisting moment.

(b) Thrust Forces

Thrust forces will tend to bend the blades of the propeller forwards in the direction of flight. This is illustrated in Fig.1-6.

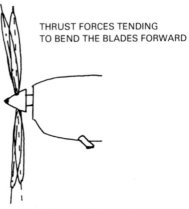

THRUST FORCES TENDING
TO BEND THE BLADES FORWARD

Fig.1-6. Thrust forces.

4

(c) Torque Forces

Torque forces will set up a bending tendency of the blades in the direction of rotation. This is shown in Fig.1-7.

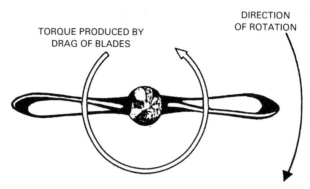

Fig.1-7. Torque forces.

(d) Air Loads

The air loads will tend to oppose the centrifugal twisting moment and coarsen blade pitch. Through design and operation the air loads and centrifugal twisting moment tend to cancel each other out.

1.5 Propeller Design

The propeller for a particular aircraft is designed to meet the specific requirements for that installation and the designer has to consider the following aspects of its operation.

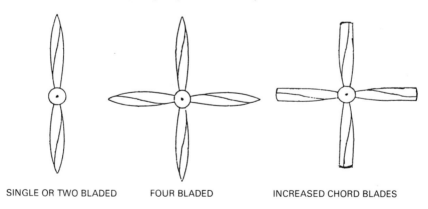

SINGLE OR TWO BLADED   FOUR BLADED   INCREASED CHORD BLADES

Fig.1-8.

(a) Propeller Diameter and Number of Blades

These factors will depend on the power the propeller is

required to absorb, the take-off thrust it is required to produce, and the noise limits which have to be met.

Large diameter propellers normally result in better performance than small diameter propellers, and the blåde area is selected to ensure that the blade lift coefficients are kept in the range where the blade sections are efficient. Wide chord blades, and/or large diameter blades, lead to heavy propellers; an increase in the number of blades may increase cost, but reduces noise. Fig.1-8 illustrates some variations in propeller blade configuration.

(b) Propeller Tip Speeds

High propeller tip speeds will absorb greater power than low tip speeds. However, if the tip speed is allowed to approach the speed of sound, the efficiency will reduce and this consideration limits the practical diameter and rotational speed combinations. High propeller tip speeds are also the primary source of propeller noise, and large diameter propellers will produce a much better performance but at the lower r.p.m. to avoid such high tip speeds.

1.6 Propeller Design Conclusions

Generally, the propeller is a compromise to satisfy the various conflicting requirements. Small two-bladed propellers, of suitable profile, are satisfactory for low powered piston engined aircraft, but for high powered piston engines or turboprops, three- or four-, and sometimes more, bladed propellers are the norm. In some cases, contra-rotating propellers are used which are normally driven through reduction gearing to enable high power engines to operate the propeller at efficient speeds.

1.7 Propeller Mounting

Firstly, the method by which the propeller assembly is mounted on the engine can be divided into two distinct methods.

(a) Tractor Propeller
This type of mounting positions the propeller on the front of the engine.

(b) Pusher Propeller
This type is mounted to the rear of the engine.

Fig.1-9 shows the two main types of mounting and a combination of the tractor and pusher types mounted in-line on a small aircraft.

A further division of propeller types can be made in the form of left-handed and right-handed propellers.

(c) Left-Handed Propeller

A left-handed propeller is one which when viewed from the cockpit rotates in an anti-clockwise direction.

From outside of the aircraft, positioned at the front, the left-handed propeller will rotate in a clockwise direction.

(d) It also follows that a right-handed propeller will be seen to rotate clockwise from the cockpit, and anti-clockwise when viewed from the front of the aircraft.

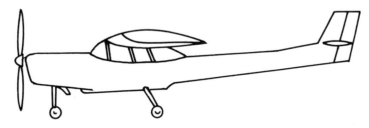

TRACTOR PROPELLER MOUNTING

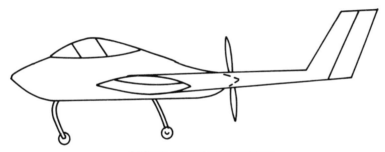

PUSHER PROPELLER MOUNTING

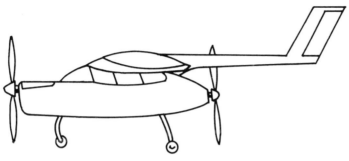

TWIN ENGINED TRACTOR AND PUSHER
MOUNTED PROPELLERS

Fig.1-9. Propeller mountings.

1.8 Consolidation

(a) General

In order to convert engine power to thrust, a piston engine requires a propeller, the thrust being obtained by accelerating an air mass, the reaction to this acceleration aft being to move the aircraft forward,

i.e. FORCE = MASS x ACCELERATION.

In terms of energy

KINETIC ENERGY = ½ MASS x VELOCITY

A propeller system gives a large air mass a small acceleration, whereas a gas turbine gives a small air mass a large acceleration. The propeller system, therefore, uses less kinetic energy than a gas turbine to achieve a given thrust.

However, due to limitations in propeller rpm and its effect on tip speed, the propeller-driven aircraft is more efficient at speeds of to 300 knots. Beyond this speed, propeller efficiency falls off rapidly due to shock waves and vibration, whereas the gas turbine aircraft becomes more efficient. Fig.1-10 shows a comparison of propulsive efficiency.

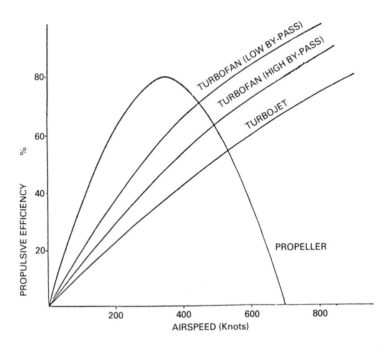

Fig.1-10. Comparison of propulsive efficiency.

(b) Propeller Terminology

The propeller rotates in a plane perpendicular to the thrust axis and, at a given point on the blade, its velocity can be represented by a vector. In relation to the blade, the relative airflow will be resultant of the rotational and aircraft velocities. Fig.1-11 shows the vectors as stated with other propeller terms.

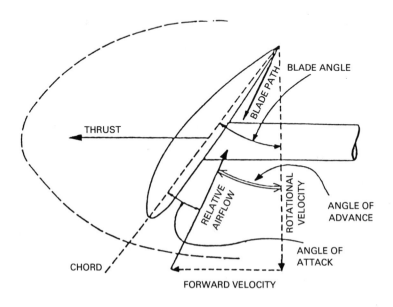

Fig. 1-11.

Angle of Advance (Helix Angle), the angle between the relative airflow and the rotational velocity.

Blade Angle, the angle between the blade face, or chord at a point and the plane of rotation.

Angle of Attack, the angle between the relative airflow and the chord.

These three angles may be linked together:

BLADE ANGLE = ANGLE OF ATTACK + ANGLE OF ADVANCE
(HELIX ANGLE)

Tractor Propeller, a propeller mounted in front of the engine.

Pusher Propeller, a propeller mounted to the rear of the engine. Air is still accelerated aft of the aircraft.

9

Ground Clearance, the clearance that exists between the propeller tip and the ground, with the aircraft in normal flying altitude.

Fuselage Clearance, the clearance between the propeller tip and the side of the fuselage; usually considered on multi-engined aircraft.

(c) Forces Acting on a Blade

Because the blade section of a propeller is an aerofoil section, its aerodynamics may be studied in a similar way using similar terms, viz: lift and drag. The aerodynamic force produced by setting the blade at a small positive angle of attack may be resolved with respect to the direction of motion of the aircraft.

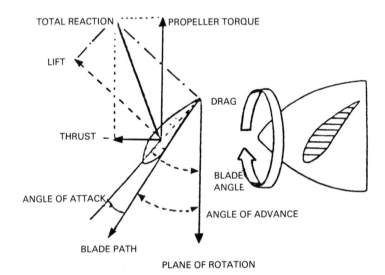

Fig. 1-12. Resolution of forces.

As can be seen in Fig.1-12, the reaction thus resolved is in the form of lift and drag vectors. Whilst the drag component is important when considering retardation effect on the blade, the breakdown of the resultant into thrust and torque is more useful. Again, as can be seen, thrust is that part of the total reaction in the direction of flight, whilst torque is the component vertical to thrust and normally opposite to rotational velocity. The thrust component is therefore the propulsive force, whilst torque tends to rotate the aircraft in the opposite direction to that produced by rotational velocity. Fig.1-12 shows this effect.

(d) Blade Twist

The rotational velocity depends on the radius of the blade. Therefore, in order to maintain an efficient angle of attack along the length of the blade it is necessary to reduce the blade angle towards the tip. This is the reason for the helical twist on a blade as shown in Fig.1-13. In effect, it can also be viewed as allowing for change of angle of advance, to keep the thrust constant along the blade length.

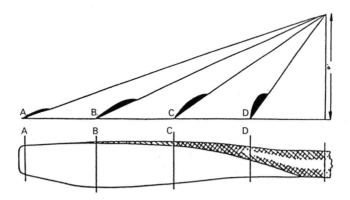

Fig.1-13. Blade twist.

(e) Centrifugal Forces

Centrifugal, bending and twisting forces act on a propeller during flight, and can be very severe at high rotational speeds. Propellers must be both strong enough to resist these forces, and rigid enough to prevent flutter. The main forces experienced are as follows.

(a) Centrifugal forces which induce radial stress in the blades and hub, and, when acting on material which is not on the blade axis, also induce a twisting moment. Centrifugal force can be resolved into two components in the plane of rotation; one is a radial force parallel to the blade axis, and the other a force at 90 degrees to the blade axis. The former produces radial stress and the latter tends to turn the blade to a finer pitch. The turning effect is referred to as centrifugal twisting moment, and is illustrated in Fig.1-14. The wider the blade, the greater will be the twisting moment.

(b) Thrust forces which tend to bend the blades forward in the direction of flight.

(c) Torque forces which tend to bend the blades against the direction of rotation.

(d) Air loads which normally tend to oppose the centrifugal twisting moment and coarsen blade pitch.

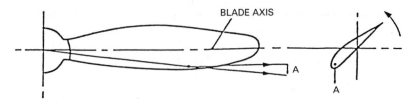

BLADE AXIS

Fig.1-14. Centrifugal Twisting Moment.

(f) Blade Angle

An aircraft having no forward velocity, with a blade having rotational velocity, the angle of advance would be zero, and the angle of attack would equal the blade angle. Once the aircraft has forward velocity, the angle of advance increases and the angle of attack decreases. As with a wing aerofoil, the optimum angle of attack is achieved at 3° to 4°. Therefore, the angle at which the blade is set (on the hub) must take into account the recommended cruise speed and operating rpm.

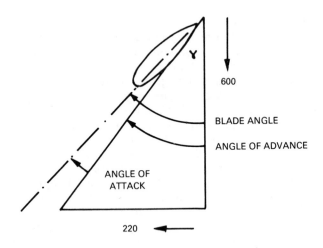

600

BLADE ANGLE

ANGLE OF ADVANCE

ANGLE OF ATTACK

220

Fig.1-15. Blade angle.

The following example, based on Fig.1-15, will illustrate this point.

and its effective pitch. Geometric pitch is the distance a propeller should advance in one complete revolution. An analogy would be the distance a screw would move into a solid during one complete turn. The effective pitch is the distance it actually advances in one 360° revolution. The effective pitch will be less because of the slippage inevitably occurring when working in the thin medium of air. See Fig.1-17.

(j) Power Absorption

The propeller must be able to absorb the power imparted to it by the engine. If engine BHP exceeds propeller torque the propeller will overspeed, and both engine and propeller become inefficient. This problem is most noticeable when climbing with high power and low forward speed.

The critical factor in matching propeller to engine power is the tip velocity. Compressibility effects decrease thrust and increases the rotational drag, thereby reducing the efficiency of the blade(s).

This consideration imposes limitations on propeller diameter, rpm and TAS as which it can be used.

Factors which may improve the ability of a propeller to absorb are:

(a) Increase blade angle and thus angle of attack

(b) Increase diameter of the propeller

(c) Increase camber of the blade aerofoil section

(d) Increase the chord of the blades

(e) Increase the number of blades

The usual method used to absorb power of the engine is to increase the "solidity" of the propeller, i.e. the ratio between that part of the propeller disc which is solid and the circumference at that radius, or, that part of the disc covered by the blades to the total area of the disc. It can be seen that an increase in solidity can be achieved by

(i) Increasing the number of blades, e.g. Contra-rotating propellers.

(ii) Increasing the chord of each blade, e.g. paddle blades.

Although the latter is easier, the low aspect ratio of the blades makes it less efficient.

(k) Swing on Take-Off

There is a tendency for propeller driven aircraft, with tail wheel undercarriage, to "swing" to one side on take-off. The causes of this tendency are:

(a) Asymmetric blade effect.

(b) Torque reaction.

(c) Slipstream effect.

(d) Gyroscopic effect.

(e) Cross-wind (weathercock) effect.

Since (e) is not a purely propeller-generated cause, it will not be considered.

In propeller-driven aircraft with tail wheel, with the propeller turning anti-clockwise when viewed from the rear, all the causes listed above will act in the same direction (assuming cross-wind from the right). However, some aircraft configurations compensate for some of the factors, e.g. nose wheel type undercarriage, contra-rotating propellers, biased directional trim, etc.

(a) **Asymmetric Blade Effect**   This effect arises from the axis of rotation being inclined in relation to the horizontal path of the aircraft when the tail wheel is town.

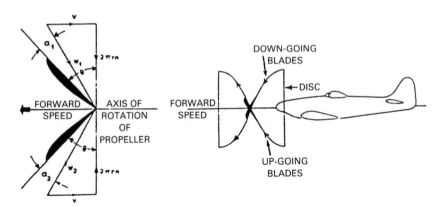

Fig.1-18. Asymmetric blade effect.

Fig.1-19 now shows how the angles of attack and resultant velocities are changed when the axis of rotation is inclined. The down-going blade has a higher angle of attack, and therefore produces more thrust than the up-going blade. Also, distance travelled in unit time by the down-going blade is greater than the up-going blade, thus the down-going blade has a higher speed relative to airflow, and for a given angle of attack produces more thrust. When the propeller is turning anti-clockwise (from rear), the left hand half of the propeller disc produces greater thrust and will yaw the aircraft to the right. Similar lift variations are produced if the propeller is yawed and not pitched.

(b) **Torque Effect** If the propeller rotates anti-clockwise (from rear) torque reaction will tend to rotate the aircraft in the opposite direction, i.e. roll to starboard. One method of counteracting this involves the use of "wash out" (wing incidence decrease) on the lifting wing, the difference in lift causing a rolling moment opposing torque reaction.

The rolling motion caused by torque is also counteracted by the main undercarriage in contact with the ground, resulting in more weight being supported on the starboard undercarriage than the port; this increases the rolling resistance of the starboard undercarriage, causing the aircraft to swing to the right until the wings take the weight off the undercarriage.

(c) **Slipstream Effect** A propeller rotating anti-clockwise will impart a rotation to the slipstream in the same sense. This rotation causes an asymmetric flow on the fin and rudder so as to induce an aerodynamic force to the left, causing the aircraft to yaw to the right. This may be overcome by off-setting the fin, or applying bias to the rudder.

(d) **Gyroscopic Effect** As the tail wheel leaves the ground, a torque is applied to the rotating propeller in a nose down sense. The effect of this torque on the angular moment of the disc is like that of a precessing gyroscope, i.e. the torque appears 90° removed from the point of application, in the direction of rotation, again producing a yaw to the right. Fig.1-20 illustrates the gyroscopic effect.

Fig.1-18 shows the condition where the propeller axis is in the line of flight. It can be seen that the speeds of each blade will be equal since angles of attack and relative air-flow on both propeller sections are equal; also, distances travelled in unit time by both up-going and down-going blade are equal.

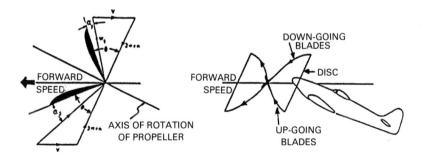

Fig.1-19. Asymmetric blade effect.

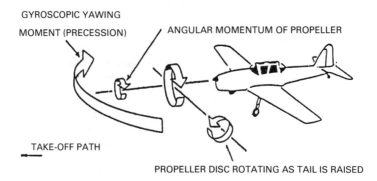

GYROSCOPIC YAWING
MOMENT (PRECESSION)

ANGULAR MOMENTUM OF PROPELLER

TAKE-OFF PATH

PROPELLER DISC ROTATING AS TAIL IS RAISED

Fig.1-20. Gyroscopic effect.

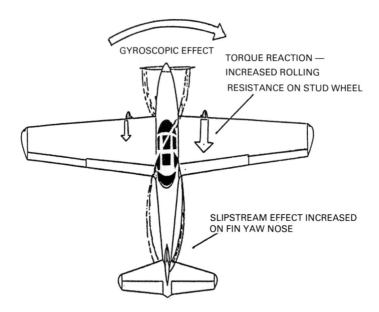

GYROSCOPIC EFFECT

TORQUE REACTION —
INCREASED ROLLING
RESISTANCE ON STUD WHEEL

SLIPSTREAM EFFECT INCREASED
ON FIN YAW NOSE

Fig.1-21. The main causes of swing on take-off.

CHAPTER 1
TEST YOURSELF QUESTIONS

1. A propeller that is mounted at the front of the engine is termed:
   - (a) a drag propeller.
   - (b) a pusher propeller.
   - (c) a thrust propeller.
   - (d) a tractor propeller.

   Ref. Ch.1. Para.1.8.

2. The blade angle is:
   - (a) equal to angle of attack plus angle of advance.
   - (b) equal to angle of advance plus the helix angle.
   - (c) equal to angle of attack plus blade incidence angle.
   - (d) equal to angle of helix plus blade incidence angle.

   Ref. Ch.1. Para.1.8.

3. Ground clearance is the distance between the:
   - (a) centre axis of the propeller and the ground.
   - (b) blade tip and the ground with the aircraft in normal flying attitude.
   - (c) blade tip and the ground with the aircraft in normal ground attitude.
   - (d) blade tip and the fuselage when the aircraft is on the ground.

   Ref. Ch.1. Para.1.8.

4. The helix angle is:
   - (a) equal to the angle of attack plus the angle of advance.
   - (b) equal to the angle of advance plus the incidence angle.
   - (c) the angle of advance.
   - (d) equal to the angle of attack plus the slip angle.

   Ref. Ch.1. Para.1.8.

5. Power absorbtion may be improved in a propeller by:
   - (a) reducing the number of blades.
   - (b) increasing the diameter of the propeller.
   - (c) reducing the chord of each blade.
   - (d) reducing the camber of the blade section.

   Ref. Ch.1. Para.1.8.

2

TYPES OF PROPELLER

2.1 Introduction

Firstly a reminder of the basic functions of the propeller. The propeller is designed to convert the turning effort of the engine into a direct push or pull along the line of flight. This push or pull is called the thrust. The propeller obtains this thrust by screwing its way through the air, in much the same way as a ship's propeller does through water. The propeller blades are generally two, three or four in number. However, on some modern advanced designs many blades may be used. The propellers are mounted in a hub which in turn is mounted on the engine propeller drive shaft. Fig.2-1 shows an example propeller and engine assembly.

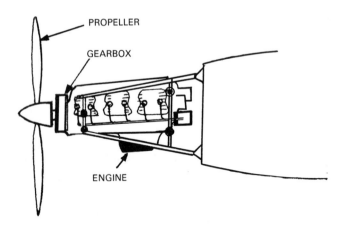

PROPELLER

GEARBOX

ENGINE

Fig.2-1. Engine and propeller assembly.

The blades are set at an angle to the plane of rotation. The distance the blades would move forward during one complete revolution if the air were solid is called the pitch. This is shown in Fig.2-2. The angle of the blade giving this forward movement is known as the blade angle. As the air is not solid, in practice the propeller always has a certain amount of slip, which means the actual distance moved forward is less than the pitch.

20

Due to the fact that the blade tips travel round a far larger path than the root ends, yet at the same time move forward the same distance, the angle at which these two portions of the blade are set will vary. The nearer the tip the less the angle, and vice-versa. This accounts for the twist of the blades as shown in Fig.2-3.

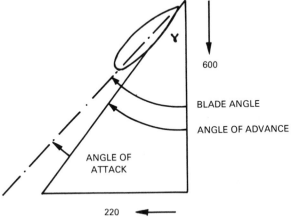

Fig.2-2. Blade angle.

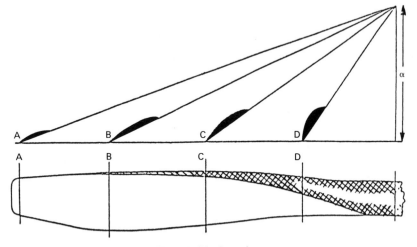

Fig.2-3. Blade twist.

2.2 Fixed Pitch Propellers

A fixed pitch propeller is a propeller assembly which has its blades fitted to the hub at a fixed, or set, angle and that angle cannot be changed in flight or on the ground. Fixed pitch propellers tend to be used in modern times on light aircraft. The efficiency of such a propeller is confined to a relatively small section of the aircraft's speed range.

2.3 Variable Pitch Propellers

This type of propeller assembly has the ability to change the pitch of its blades in flight, or on the ground. There are various types of variable pitch propeller and in general they are designed to provide greater flexibility and efficiency over a much wider aircraft speed range than that of the fixed pitch propeller. Details of the construction and operation of the variable pitch propeller and its operating and control mechanism is discussed later. However, here follows a basic general description of an example assembly.

2.4 Basic Operation of a Variable Pitch Propeller

The primary cockpit controls to consider are those of the engine throttle, which controls the engine power setting, and the R.P.M. Control Lever. The R.P.M. (revolutions per minute) Control Lever enables the pilot to select the required engine speed within the pitch range of the propeller. The R.P.M. Control Lever is connected to a control unit, known as the Constant Speed Unit (C.S.U.), that is mounted on and driven by the engine.

Once a particular engine speed has been selected, the C.S.U. acts as a governor unit and maintains the selected engine speed, within the power available.

For example:

Engine speed increases. Through the propeller drive shaft, the propeller r.p.m. will also increase. The propeller r.p.m. increase will be sensed by the C.S.U., which will move the propeller blade angle to a coarser angle which in turn will make the propeller do more work, increasing the load on the engine and so causing engine r.p.m. to reduce, thereby maintaining the selected r.p.m. on the R.P.M. Control Lever. In the event engine speed reduces, the opposite will happen.

It can be seen from the above statements that the engine speed can be controlled automatically, removing the task from the pilot of constantly adjusting engine r.p.m. This will also reduce the wear rate on the engine.

2.5 Single Acting Variable Pitch Propeller (Constant Speed)

There are two basic types of constant speed propeller operating mechanisms. They are referred to as the Single acting propeller and the Double acting propeller. The term single acting essentially refers to the pitch change system utilizing engine oil pressure to operate the pitch change cylinder and move the propeller blades to fine pitch and normally a combination of centrifugal force and spring pressure moves the propeller blades to coarse pitch. The following chapter explains the operation of the constant speed unit in conjunction with this type of unit.

2.6   Double Acting Variable Pitch Propeller (Constant Speed)

As this is the most common type of constant speed propeller used on larger commercial aircraft, a separate chapter has been devoted to its operation and also the operation of its associated constant speed unit.

CHAPTER 2
TEST YOURSELF QUESTIONS

1. The blade angle:
    (a) is constant throughout the propeller blade length.
    (b) is greatest at the blade root.
    (c) is equal to the angle of advance.
    (d) is greatest at the blade tip.

    Ref. Ch.2. Para.2.1.

2. A variable pitch constant speed propeller is designed primarily to:
    (a) maintain the propeller at constant thrust.
    (b) maintain the propeller at constant r.p.m.
    (c) maintain the propeller at constant pitch.
    (d) maintain the engine at constant r.p.m.

    Ref. Ch.2. Para.2.4.

3. In a single acting propeller of the variable pitch type:
    (a) the pitch change is limited to a specific range and not totally variable.
    (b) the pitch change is activated hydraulically in both directions.
    (c) the pitch change is activated hydraulically in one direction.
    (d) the pitch change mechanism is manually operated.

    Ref. Ch.2. Para.2.5.

4. A variable pitch constant speed propeller:
    (a) eliminates the need for constant adjustment to angle r.p.m.
    (b) eliminates the need for constant adjustment to propeller pitch.
    (c) eliminates the need for constant changes to mixture setting.
    (d) eliminates the need for constant boost adjustment.

    Ref. Ch.2. Para.2.4.

5. The pitch is controlled on a constant speed variable pitch propeller:

    (a) by the r.p.m. lever.

    (b) by the throttle.

    (c) by the C.S.U.

    (d) by the governor spring.

Ref. Ch.2. Para.2.4.

3

BASIC VARIABLE PITCH REQUIREMENTS

3.1 Introduction

Variable pitch propellers fall primarily into two basic types, those which have a limited ability to vary their pitch, i.e. perhaps only two or three basic positions to satisfy certain requirements such as engine starting, where minimum propeller drag is required; and take-off where high engine r.p.m. is required coupled with a compromise pitch position, that is high power with propeller drag kept as low as possible, and finally a cruise position.

Generally it is only the larger and more complex propellers which have a "feathering" facility.

The second type of variable pitch propeller is the constant speed type which is designed to minimize the adjustments the pilot would normally have to make to the engine throttle in flight to maintain constant r.p.m. on the engine which in turn will also improve engine fuel consumption and reduce wear on the engine.

The advantages of the fully variable pitch constant speed propeller are many and varied. Different manufacturers achieve the various functions in different ways and so the following paragraphs give a general description of the primary functions of a constant speed variable pitch propeller.

3.2 Extra fine or fully fine pitch

In order to ease the task of engine starting, it is useful to reduce the air loads, i.e. drag on the propeller blades, as much as possible. This can be achieved by turning the blades to the finest pitch possible. This pitch setting is ground fine, or also known as extra fine. In this position the load on the engine caused by the propeller is reduced to an absolute minimum, and also the load on the electrical starting system is also reduced.

Whilst this position is suitable for engine starting once the engine is running, there is a serious danger of the engine overheating as the propeller in this position will be generating minimum thrust, therefore minimum airflow over the engine for cooling purposes will also be the case. As a result, once the engine has started and the throttle is opened the blades automatically will increase pitch into normal fine. A set of stops immediately spring into place, preventing the propeller accidentally moving back into the extra fine or ground fine pitch. In flight the stops also prevent the propeller moving into extra fine as in such a position with reduced blade drag, engine overspeeding is likely to occur. The correct or official name given to these stops are fine pitch stops or flight fine pitch stops and their primary function is to prevent the propeller moving into extra fine in flight, i.e. they are withdrawn for engine starting, allowing the propeller to move into extra fine.

·3.3 Constant Speed Range

As the throttle is opened above a certain r.p.m., the fine pitch stops are over-ridden (passed) and the engine and propeller blades are now out of the extra fine range, and the propeller moves into the constant speed range.

Prior to moving into the constant speed range, the throttle must be set to the required setting and the r.p.m. lever set. The throttle setting controls the engine power required, as in the situation of any piston engine.

The r.p.m. lever controls the setting on the governor of the constant speed unit. Details of the operation of the constant speed unit are given later, at this point a brief description only is given.

To maintain the engine at constant r.p.m., virtually eliminating the pilot's need to constantly adjust the throttle to maintain constant engine r.p.m., the propeller will adjust its pitch to increase or decrease the load on the propeller and hence the load on the engine. If the engine r.p.m. start to fall, propeller pitch will reduce, reducing load on the engine, allowing the engine to speed up and return to its original r.p.m.

If the engine starts to increase r.p.m. (overspeed), propeller pitch will increase and therefore increase the load on the engine, thus reducing engine r.p.m. When the propeller is in the constant speed range it is prevented from moving into the extra fine pitch by stops and is also prevented from moving into the feathered position by feathering stops.

Prevention of the propeller moving into extra fine or ground fine is by the fine pitch stops. Prevention of the propeller moving into the feathered position is by the coarse pitch stops.

Fig.3-1 shows a simple sketch of stop sequence.

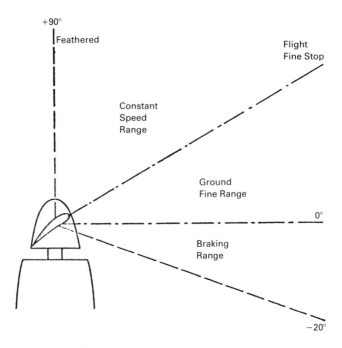

Fig.3-1. Propeller blade positions.

3.4 Feathered Position

The propeller may have to be feathered in the event of an engine or propeller drive malfunction. This is essentially an emergency function where the engine is stopped and the blade pitch moved beyond the coarse stops into the feathered position to stop the windmilling action and any further damage to the engine. It is equally important that the propeller must not come out of the feathered position by accident as this may result in serious damage to the engine and also create assymetric problems in controlling the aircraft.

CHAPTER 3
TEST YOURSELF QUESTIONS

1. Prior to engine starting:
    (a) coarse pitch is selected to give maximum cooling airflow.
    (b) extra fine pitch is selected to reduce the load on the engine.
    (c) extra fine pitch is selected to increase cooling airflow over the engine.
    (d) fine pitch is selected to reduce the load on the engine.
                                            Ref. Ch.3. Para.3.2.

2. After the engine has started, the propeller:
    (a) remains in its selected position until take-off.
    (b) moves into fine pitch to increase airflow.
    (c) moves into coarse pitch to increase cooling airflow.
    (d) moves into the feathered position until engine operating temperature has been attained.
                                            Ref. Ch.3. Para.3.2.

3. The constant speed range is normally between:
    (a) extra fine and fully coarse pitch.
    (b) fine and coarse pitch.
    (c) fine and feathered positions.
    (d) extra fine and feathered positions.
                                            Ref. Ch.3. Para.3.3.

4. In the feathered position:
    (a) the leading edge of the blade faces forward.
    (b) the trailing edge of the blade faces forward.
    (c) the thrust face faces forward.
    (d) the pressure face faces forward.
                                    Ref. Ch.3. Para.3.3. diag-3.2.

5. In flight:
    (a) the blades may move to extra fine.
    (b) the blades may move into feathered if the engine overspeeds.
    (c) the blades cannot move into extra fine.
    (d) the blades cannot be selected out of the constant speed range.
                                            Ref. Ch.3. Para.3.2.

4
SINGLE ACTING VARIABLE PITCH PROPELLER (PISTON ENGINES)

4.1 Introduction

The construction of a variable pitch propeller has basically been discussed in previous chapters. In this chapter, however, construction differences will be discussed to provide a clear understanding of the single and double acting propeller types. The double acting type is discussed in detail in Chapter 6.

4.2 Principle of Operation

An example of a single acting propeller is shown in Fig.4-1 and is a constant speed, feathering type propeller and is commonly

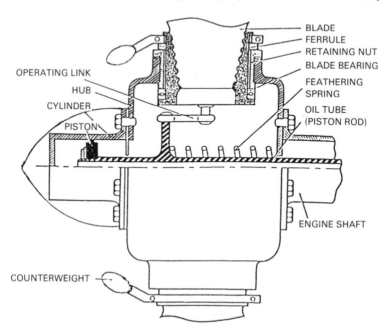

Fig.4-1. Single-acting propeller.

fitted to small and medium-size aircraft, usually twin-engine types.

On some propeller types the pitch change operating mechanism directs oil under pressure through a hollow tube, or piston rod, to the front of the piston, which moves the piston to the rear to turn the blades to a finer pitch; on other propeller types the reverse applies. With the propeller in fine pitch, held by the oil pressure, when the oil pressure is reduced, or released, the counterweights and feathering spring move the piston forward, which in turn moves the blades to coarser pitch. The counterweights produce a centrifugal twisting moment, but because they are positioned at 90° to the chord line, they tend to move the blades to coarse pitch. The counterweights must be located far enough from the blade axis, and must be heavy enough to overcome the natural twisting moment of the blades. However, since weight and space are limiting factors, they tend only to be used with blades of narrow chord.

4.3 Propeller Blade Control

The blade angle is controlled by a constant speed unit which comprises a centrifugal governor, a governor valve assembly, and an oil pump which boosts oil pressure from the engine lubrication system sufficiently for the operation of the propeller pitch change mechanism. The governor is driven by the engine via an ancillary drive, and movement of the governor weights under centrifugal force is opposed by a control spring. The loading on the control spring is set by movement of the pilot's control lever, that is the R.P.M. Lever. Fig.4-2 shows the R P.M. Lever and its selection positions.

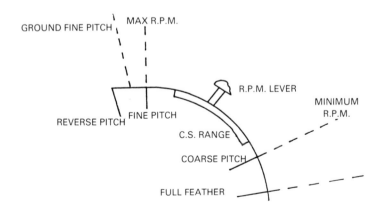

Fig.4-2. R.P.M. control positions.

The position of the governor valve is determined, therefore, by engine speed and the force exerted by the spring; when these forces balance, the oil line to the propeller is closed, and oil is trapped in the cylinder of the pitch change mechanism.

4.4 Operation

When the pilot's R.P.M. Control Lever is set to the maximum r.p.m. position, and the throttle is at a low power setting, the governor valve will be in the fully down position. Oil from the pump will be directed through the hollow piston rod to turn the propeller blades to fully fine pitch. As the throttle is opened and r.p.m. increases, centrifugal force on the governor weights will cause the valve to rise until a position is reached where maximum r.p.m. is reached and the oil line to the propeller is closed. Any further increase in power will tend to increase r.p.m. and result in the governor valve being lifted and oil will drain from the propeller and cause the blades to move to a coarser pitch to maintain the set r.p.m. by placing a greater load on the propeller.

During flight, rearward movement of the pilot's control lever (R.P.M. LEVER) will reduce spring loading, and allow the governor weights to lift the valve. This will result in a coarser blade angle, resulting in a greater load on the propeller and hence on the engine, which will reduce engine speed until the spring force is balanced by centrifugal force on the governor weights. Forward movement of the pilot's control lever will increase spring loading and result in a finer propeller pitch and higher engine speed.

If the propeller load decreases in flight, or power is increased, the engine will begin to speed up, the governor weights will lift the valve and the propeller pitch will move to coarse to maintain the set engine speed. Conversely, an increase in propeller load, or a decrease in engine power, will result in a finer propeller pitch to maintain the set engine speed. Remember, the objectives of the constant speed unit is to maintain constant engine speed, not constant propeller speed.

4.5 Feathering

On smaller aircraft, such as those fitted with a single acting propeller, feathering is accomplished by moving the pilot's control lever to the appropriate position, which is normally obtained by moving the lever through a gate in the quadrant. This action raises the governor valve fully, allowing oil to drain from the propeller, and the blades will turn to the fully coarse position (feathered) under the action of the counterweights and spring.

In order to unfeather the propeller, a separate source of oil under pressure is required, On light aircraft this is usually provided by an accumulator, which is charged during normal flight. To unfeather, the pilot's control lever is moved into the constant speed range, thus lowering the governor valve, and the unfeathering button is pressed, releasing oil from the accumulator and allowing it to flow to the propeller. This action commences unfeathering, and once the propeller starts to windmill the normal oil supply completes the operation.

When the engine is stopped on the ground, oil pressure in the cylinder is gradually relieved by leakage through the constant speed unit, and this would enable the propeller blades to turn to the feathered position under action of the feathering springs. This would result in unacceptable loads on the propeller for engine starting, and so a centrifugal latch is fitted to prevent forward movement of the propeller piston when the engine is stopped. The basic operation of the centrifugal latch is shown in Fig.4-3.

4.6 Centrifugal Latch

The centrifugal latch is fitted to some types of constant speed propeller to prevent the propeller blades moving into the feathered position when the aircraft is on the ground as the engine is switched off.

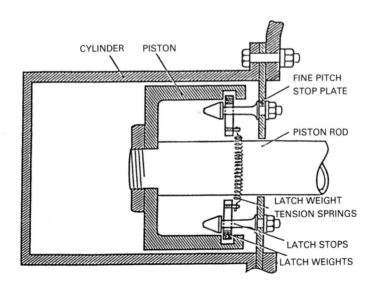

Fig.4-3. Centrifugal latch.

Centrifugal force disengages the latch at all speeds above ground idle therefore enabling the propeller function normally during flight. Below this speed, however, centrifugal force is overcome by return springs and the piston can only move a short distance, normally equivalent to approximately five degrees of blade angle. When the engine is started, oil pressure builds up to move the blades to fully fine pitch and centrifugal force disengages the latch.

CHAPTER 4
TEST YOURSELF QUESTIONS

1. On a single acting variable pitch propeller:
    (a) spring pressure changes the pitch in both directions.
    (b) oil pressure changes the pitch in both directions.
    (c) the blades have no fixed constant speed range.
    (d) the blades are operated by the piston assembly.

    Ref. Ch.4. Para.4.2.

2. Centrifugal latches are fitted to some types of variable pitch propellers to:
    (a) permit the blades to move into the fully fine position in flight.
    (b) prevent the blades moving into the feathered position when the engine is switched off.
    (c) prevent the blades moving into the feathered position in flight.
    (d) permit the blades going into reverse pitch in flight.

    Ref. Ch.4. Para.4.6.

3. On engine start-up:
    (a) the blades are already in fully fine pitch.
    (b) the oil pressure builds up and moves the blades to fully fine.
    (c) the oil pressure builds up and moves the blades to coarse pitch.
    (d) the blades will remain locked in their previous position.

    Ref. Ch.4. Para.4.6.

4. Normally on a single acting propeller, feathering is accomplished by:
    (a) moving the R.P.M. Lever fully forward.
    (b) moving the R.P.M. Lever to the feather position.
    (c) pushing the feathering button.
    (d) selecting the booster pump "ON".

    Ref. Ch.4. Para.4.5.

5. On a single acting variable pitch propeller:
    (a) the counterweights create a centrifugal twisting moment.

(b) the counterweights compensate for a centrifugal twisting moment.

(c) the counterweights assist in moving the blades to a finer pitch.

(d) the counterweights prevent blade flutter.

Ref. Ch.4. Para.4.2.

5
PISTON ENGINE CONSTANT SPEED UNIT
As used with a Single Acting Propeller

5.1 Introduction

A variable pitch propeller theoretically permits the pitch to be so adjusted that the engine is running at the r.p.m. best suited for the particular conditions of flight. For any given pitch, altered conditions of flight effect the propeller efficiency and hence the engine r.p.m., thus calling for constant readjustment. The constant speed unit effects this automatically and so relieves the pilot of the responsibility of continually altering the propeller pitch to maintain the r.p.m. at the desired figure.

It should be noted that the primary function of the constant speed unit is to maintain the engine r.p.m. at the figure selected on the R.P.M. Control Lever in the cockpit. It does this by altering the pitch of the propeller blades, but the particular pitch required for any given r.p.m. will vary with the flight conditions. The constant speed unit maintains r.p.m. constant, not pitch constant.

Fig.5-1 shows the construction and operation of a constant speed unit.

The following should be read in conjunction with reference to Fig.5-1.

5.2 Description

A hollow shaft driven by the engine, drives a driving plate on which are pivoted two flyweights, restrained against centrifugal force by the governor springs. A cup mounted on the driving plate prevents the weights flying out too far. The weights act on a piston valve which fits inside the hollow drive shaft and serves to control the flow of oil to the propeller.

Also driven by the shaft is a gear type oil pump, sometimes referred to as a booster pump, which receives oil from the engine lubrication system oil pump and increases its pressure to the required value; a relief valve prevents excessive pressure.

The pilot-operated R.P.M. Control Lever varies the load on the

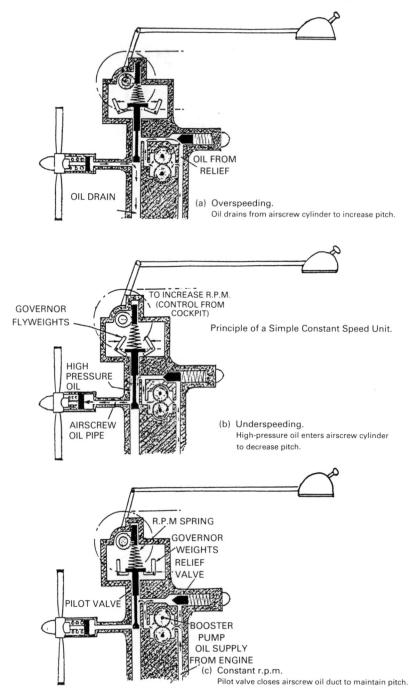

OIL FROM RELIEF

OIL DRAIN

(a) Overspeeding.
Oil drains from airscrew cylinder to increase pitch.

GOVERNOR FLYWEIGHTS

TO INCREASE R.P.M. (CONTROL FROM COCKPIT)

Principle of a Simple Constant Speed Unit.

HIGH PRESSURE OIL

AIRSCREW OIL PIPE

(b) Underspeeding.
High-pressure oil enters airscrew cylinder to decrease pitch.

R.P.M SPRING
GOVERNOR WEIGHTS
RELIEF VALVE

PILOT VALVE

BOOSTER PUMP OIL SUPPLY FROM ENGINE

(c) Constant r.p.m.
Pilot valve closes airscrew oil duct to maintain pitch.

Fig.5-1.

upper end of the governor spring through a rack and pinion mechanism, or a bell crank lever.

5.3 Operation

While the engine is running at the desired r.p.m. the piston valve will be in the neutral position, closing all oil ports to the propeller. The centrifugal force of the flyweights just balances the compression of the governor spring in this position.

(a) If the engine r.p.m. rises:
The flyweights will fly outwards, raising the piston valve and opening the ports. This will allow oil flow, which will be in the direction to cause the propeller blades to move to a coarser pitch. The coarser pitch will increase the load on the engine, the engine r.p.m. will reduce, and the piston valve will return to the neutral position as the spring pushes it down against the reduced centrifugal force of the flyweights.

(b) If the engine r.p.m. falls:
The spring pressure will be greater than the reduced centrifugal force of the flyweights and will force the piston valve down. The oil flow will now be in the direction of making the propeller blade's pitch finer. The engine will speed up and the increased centrifugal force will cause the flyweights to return the piston valve to neutral.

(c) Increasing r.p.m. in flight:
Should the pilot wish to increase r.p.m., he will move the R.P.M. Control Lever forward. This action will compress the governor spring through the rack and pinion mechanism, the centrifugal force of the flyweights no longer balances the increased spring pressure, and the piston valve is forced down. The propeller blade pitch is made finer and so reduces the load on the engine and the engine r.p.m. will rise until the centrifugal force of the flyweights can balance the spring pressure and return the piston to neutral. The r.p.m. is now maintained automatically at the new selected value. Should the pilot wish to reduce r.p.m., then the reverse operation will take place.

(d) Feathering.
On some constant speed systems, the last portion of movement on the cockpit mounted R.P.M. Control Lever in the decrease speed direction causes the spring control to engage with a stop on the upper end of the piston valve and thus raise the valve positively. The governor is now out of action and the piston becomes coarser until the propeller blades are fully feathered.

6

DOUBLE ACTING PROPELLERS

6.1 Introduction

In general, apart from the operating mechanism, these propellers are similar in design to the single acting type. The primary difference between the single acting type, in which the pitch change action is by hydraulic pressure to move the propeller blades from coarse pitch to fine pitch and spring and centrifugal force to move the blades into coarse pitch from fine, is that in the double acting type hydraulic pressure is used to operate the pitch change in both directions. In the double acting type the cylinder remains stationary and the piston moves, provision is also sometimes made for feathering. Fig.6-1 shows an example of a double acting propeller.

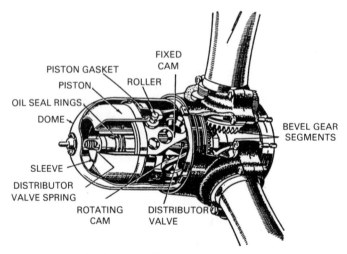

Fig.6-1. Double acting propeller.

6.2 Construction and Operation

The blades and hub are similar in design to the single acting type propeller assembly. The brackets on the root end of the blades are replaced in this type by bevel gear segments which are coupled to the blades by leaf springs which pre-load the gear teeth. The hub is retained on the engine drive shaft by a separate nut. The piston slides in the dome which is attached to the hub by dowels and a retaining nut. Passing through its centre is the distributor valve which is attached to the propeller shaft. An oil seal round the circumference of the piston, and oil seal rings on the distributor valve which bear on the sleeve attached to the piston, prevent oil from passing from one side of the piston to the other. The piston is guided by four sets of rollers attached to it, which slide in the right hand helical slots in the fixed cam ring which is attached to the dome. Inside and concentric with the fixed cam is the rotating cam, which has a bevel gear formed at its rear end, meshing with the bevel gear segments on the blade. This cam has four left handed helical slots in it in which the rollers attached to the piston also work. Ball races support the rotating cam and take the end thrust; stops are fitted to limit the blade movement.

Note:–

(a) The helical slots are as shown for a left-handed propeller. However, for a right-handed propeller they are reversed in hand.

(b) For Feathering propellers, the helical slots are extended beyond the normal coarse pitch position, but at a reduced pitch. This reduction of angularity decreases the effectiveness of the cam mechanism and requires a higher pressure than normal to operate the rotating cam. This arrangement will only allow the blades to be feathered by applying this higher pressure, which is provided by a separate pump. Accidental feathering due to a defect in the constant speed unit is prevented.

6.3   Distributor Valve

The inner oil tube extension of the distributor valve housing screws into the engine propeller shaft and retains the valve in position. When fully home, the base of the housing seats on the outer oil tube inside the propeller shaft, a washer making an oil tight joint. Normally, engine oil pressure passes through the inner oil tube, through the distributor valve, and so to the front of the piston. "Boosted oil pressure" from the oil pump in the constant speed unit passes through the annular space between the outer and inner oil tubes, through the distributor valve, and so to the back of the piston.

The spring loaded piston type valves housed in the distributor valve housing operates only during the unfeathering operation.

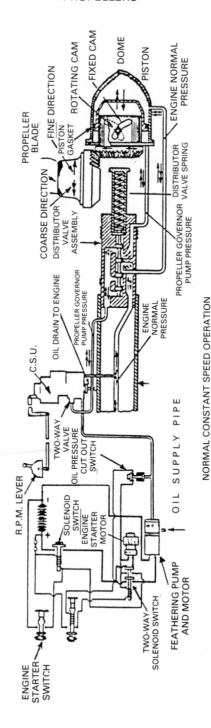

NORMAL CONSTANT SPEED OPERATION

Fig.6-2.

6.4 Operation

(a) Movement to Coarse Pitch

In order to move the propeller blades to coarse pitch, "boosted" oil pressure from the constant speed unit oil pump, sometimes called the booster pump, is admitted to the back of the piston. The piston is forced forwards and its guide rollers acting in the slots of the fixed cam cause it to rotate. At the same time the forward movement of the rollers in the slots in the rotating cam force that cam to rotate. As the slots in the fixed and rotating cam are of opposite "hands", the rotation of the piston causes the rotating cam to turn further in the same direction: the blades are turned in their sockets by means of the bevel gears. See Fig.6-2.

(b) Movement to Fine Pitch

To turn the blades to fine pitch, the "boosted" oil pressure is cut off, the oil behind the piston is allowed to drain to the engine sump, and the engine oil pressure acting on the front of the piston forces the piston backwards, and turns the blades through the medium of the rollers, cams and bevel gears. The inherent tendency of the blades to turn to fine pitch under the influence of centrifugal force assists this operation.

(c) Feathering the Propeller on the Ground

To feather the propeller when testing it on the ground, the cockpit control lever is pushed fully forward, with a low throttle setting, and the feathering switch pressed. This starts an electric motor which drives a separate oil pump supplying oil at extra high pressure to the constant speed unit through a two-way valve which is automatically pushed over to close the normal oil passage to and from the piston valve and to admit the extra high pressure to the passage leading to the back of the piston. The extra high pressure passes to the back of the piston and feathers the blades. When fully feathered, the oil pressure builds up and operates the oil pressure cut-out switch to break the circuit and switch off the motor. See Fig.6-3.

(d) Unfeathering the Propeller

To unfeather the propeller, the cockpit control lever is pulled back, the feathering switch is pressed and held in. This prevents the high oil pressure developed switching off the motor. The pressure acting on this distributor valve forces it forward against the spring. This reverses the oil circuit

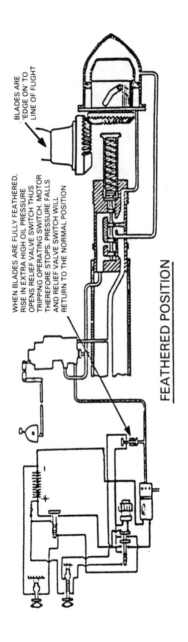

BLADES ARE 'EDGE ON' TO LINE OF FLIGHT

WHEN BLADES ARE FULLY FEATHERED, RISE IN EXTRA HIGH OIL PRESSURE OPENS RELIEF VALVE SWITCH THUS TRIPPING OPERATING SWITCH. MOTOR THEREFORE STOPS. PRESSURE FALLS AND RELIEF VALVE SWITCH WILL RETURN TO THE NORMAL POSITION

FEATHERED POSITION

Fig.6-3.

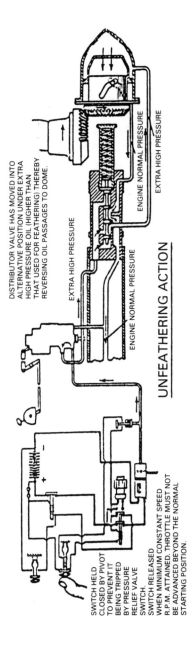

DISTRIBUTOR VALVE HAS MOVED INTO ALTERNATIVE POSITION UNDER EXTRA HIGH PRESSURE OIL (HIGHER THAN THAT USED FOR FEATHERING) THEREBY REVERSING OIL PASSAGES TO DOME.

EXTRA HIGH PRESSURE

ENGINE NORMAL PRESSURE

EXTRA HIGH PRESSURE

ENGINE NORMAL PRESSURE

SWITCH HELD CLOSED BY PIVOT TO PREVENT IT BEING TRIPPED BY PRESSURE RELIEF VALVE SWITCH.

SWITCH RELEASED WHEN MINIMUM CONSTANT SPEED R.P.M. ATTAINED. THROTTLE MUST NOT BE ADVANCED BEYOND THE NORMAL STARTING POSITION.

UNFEATHERING ACTION

Fig.6-4.

through the distributor valve, the high pressure oil is directed to the front of the piston, and the blades are unfeathered. When the desired speed is obtained by the propeller "windmilling" the engine, release the feathering switch. See Fig.6-4.

Notes:–

(a) When testing on the ground, it is unnecessary to stop the engine, but it should not be run for more than a few seconds with the propeller feathered.

(b) The feathering motor requires a very large current and, to avoid running the aircraft battery down, a ground starter battery should be coupled up to the aircraft for ground testing.

CHAPTER 6
TEST YOURSELF QUESTIONS

1. A double acting propeller utilizes:
   - (a) oil pressure to change the pitch angle in one direction only.
   - (b) oil pressure to change the pitch angle in both directions.
   - (c) oil pressure to operate in one direction and spring pressure in the other.
   - (d) a double piston assembly to provide an emergency back-up should one piston fail.

   Ref. Ch.6. Para.6.1.

2. Normally when feathering a double acting variable pitch propeller:
   - (a) the extra high oil pressure required is provided by the booster pump in the C.S.U.
   - (b) the extra high oil pressure required is provided by an electrically operated pump.
   - (c) the oil pressure required is provided by the engine lubrication system.
   - (d) the oil pressure will dissipate and the spring will move the blades to the feathered position.

   Ref. Ch.6. Para.6.4.

3. The inherent tendency of the blades of a propeller is:
   - (a) to remain in their selected position until hydraulic force is applied.
   - (b) to move toward coarse pitch.
   - (c) to hunt.
   - (d) to move toward fine pitch.

   Ref. Ch.6. Para.6.4.

4. Hydraulic oil flow control is directed by:
   - (a) the r.p.m. selector.
   - (b) the throttle valve.
   - (c) the distributor valve.
   - (d) the two-way valve.

   Ref. Ch.6. Para.6.3.

5. Movement of the blades to coarse pitch requires an oil supply from:

    (a) the engine driven pump only.

    (b) the electrically operated pump.

    (c) the booster pump.

    (d) the spring return side of the piston.

Ref. Ch.6. Para.6.4.

7

FEATHERING PROPELLERS (PISTON ENGINED AIRCRAFT)

7.1 Introduction

In the event of engine failure, or an unserviceability which requires the engine to be shut down, the feathering of the propeller may be required. Not all propellers have the ability to be feathered. However, in the event that such a facility is available, an example procedure is given below.

7.2 Example Feathering Procedure

Feathering is the procedure by which the propeller blades can be turned until, with the blade chord lines almost parallel to the airflow, there are no rotating forces acting on the propeller blades as a whole. Fig.7-1 shows the position of the propeller blade relative to the hub.

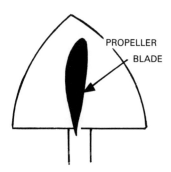

Fig.7-1. Feathered position.

In the event of engine failure and the engine ignition is switched off, the airflow passing through the propeller will continue to turn the engine over, that is rotate the engine, and such action may cause considerable damage. If the propeller is feathered it can be seen the propeller will be stationary and therefore no further damage will be inflicted on the engine.

7.3 Reduction of Drag

By feathering the propeller on a failed engine, considerable drag that would otherwise be created can be avoided.

7.4 Feathering Action

On hydraulically operated propellers, feathering may in an emergency be carried out by an electrically driven high pressure oil pump. This pump is independent of the engine and can be used whether the engine is running or not. The pump is normally operated by pressing a push button in the cockpit. On electrically operated propellers the feathering motor is activated by a feathering switch in the cockpit.

7.5 Feathering Operation (Piston Engined Aircraft)

All feathering mechanisms obtain their motive power for feathering from the electrical services of the aircraft. The propeller blades are moved through a large angle at a much greater rate than in normal constant speed operation. The process of feathering and unfeathering imposes a severe drain on aircraft batteries unless the generators are charging satisfactorily.

Example Feathering Procedure:

(a) Close the throttle on the engine of the propeller which is to be feathered.

(b) Push the appropriate feathering switch or button.

(c) Turn off the fuel supply to that engine and switch off the booster pump to that engine.

(d) If the failed engine is on fire, operate the correct fire extinguisher but only after the propeller has stopped rotating.

(e) Switch off the ignition of the dead engine.

Note: Operation of the fire extinguisher before the propeller has stopped rotating will normally result in the extinguishant being blown out of the engine bay by the engine cooling air preventing the extinguishant from doing its job of extinguishing the fire.

7.6 General Variations

The basic feathering drill given above is standard practice.

However, the feathering operation of piston engine driven propellers will vary according to the type of propeller fitted to the aircraft.

The most important differences are as follows:

(a) With some types the propeller is feathered by operating the push button only, while with other types it is necessary to move the r.p.m. control lever through a feathering gate to the feathering position before the push button is depressed.

(b) Some push buttons must be held in manually during the feathering operation; others are operated by a solenoid, and after pressure is released they will remain in until feathering is completed. If this type is fitted, the pilot must ensure that the push button springs out when feathering is complete. If it does not, it must be pulled out by hand.

(c) Electrically operated propellers feather at a slower rate than hydraulic propellers when the switch is moved to the feather position. When the blades reach the feathered position the current to the electric motor is automatically switched off.

Feathering is an emergency action and should be practiced until it is instinctive and automatic.

7.7 Unfeathering

Other than practice and test feathering, a propeller is only feathered after engine failure or as a safeguard when low engine oil pressure or excessive engine temperature is indicated, which may lead to a possible defect. In such circumstances an engine should not be restarted in flight. When unfeathering for practice or if, having regard to the reason for which the propeller was feathered in the first place, the pilot considers that the circumstances nevertheless justify restarting the engine, this should be done at a safe speed and/or height. If this is not done difficulty may be experienced owing to the increased critical speed resulting from the additional drag of the windmilling propeller while under conditions of asymmetric power.

7.8 Unfeathering in Flight

An example unfeathering sequence in flight is as follows:

(a) Set the throttle in the fully closed position. The throttle should not be moved from this position until the propeller reaches its peak windmilling r.p.m. If the throttle is opened before peak windmilling r.p.m., a fire may result from a blowback through the carburettor.

(b) Set the R.P.M. control lever just forward of the minimum r.p.m. position, or just out of the feathering gate.

(c) Switch on the ignition.

(d) Operate the feathering push button or switch. When the correct r.p.m. is reached, the pilot should check that the feathering push button is fully out; it must be pulled out by hand if it has not come out automatically.

(e) Turn on the fuel supply and switch on the booster pump if fitted.

(f) Warm up the engine and then return to the normal constant speed conditions.

7.9   Unfeathering on the ground

The following is a procedure which is normally used when unfeathering a propeller on the ground after a practiced feathered landing:

(a) The stopped engine should be restarted with its propeller still in the feathered position. This avoids discharging oil from the unfeathering propeller into the engine sump while the scavenge pump is not working.

(b) The controls should be set and the engine started in the normal manner. When the engine is running steadily, and the propeller has not started to unfeather, the feathering push button should be pushed in. When the propeller has moved from its feathered position, the push button should be released, if applicable.

In many cases the propeller will start to unfeather without the push buttons being pressed, but when this occurs on some installations pressing the push button will first cause the propeller to refeather before it finally unfeathers. If difficulty is found in starting certain engines due to the high drag of the fully feathered propeller, it may be partially unfeathered first. This should not be done if there is any evidence that flooding of the crankcase may result. This will be indicated by oil being ejected through the crankcase breathers immediately after starting. With radial engines there is a danger of hydraulic locking when starting in this manner, and these engines should be started as soon as the propeller is partially unfeathered. If for any reason an immediate attempt cannot be made to start the engine, or an attempt is made to start and the engine fails to turn over through one complete revolution of the propeller when the starter is operated, no further attempt to start should be made until a check for hydraulic locking, by hand turning, has been carried out.

7.10   Practice and Test Feathering

Feathering should not be practiced or tested if the air temperature is below minus 15 degrees C. Most aircraft are limited to a specific number of practice feathering and unfeathering cycles in a given flight. A typical example would be twelve in a training situation.

Care should be taken on multi-engined aircraft that are fitted with one generator on one engine that limited practice feathering is carried out on the engine with the generator or a severe drain may be made on the batteries. It is also advisable to switch off all unnecessary electrical loads to reduce the loads on the batteries when practice feathering.

A watch should be kept on the oil temperature of the engine with the propeller feathered to ensure the temperature of the oil is not allowed to fall too low before the engine is unfeathered.

CHAPTER 7
TEST YOURSELF QUESTIONS

1. Prior to feathering the propeller:
   - (a) firstly turn off the fuel supply to the engine.
   - (b) close the throttle to the engine of the propeller which is to be feathered.
   - (c) in the event of an engine fire, operate the extinguisher.
   - (d) in the event of fire, push the appropriate feathering button.

   Ref. Ch.7. Para.7.5.

2. When unfeathering a propeller, the:
   - (a) unfeathering button should be pressed first.
   - (b) feathering button should be pressed first.
   - (c) ignition should be switched on first.
   - (d) turn on the fuel supply first.

   Ref. Ch.7. Para.7.7.

3. When unfeathering a propeller, normally:
   - (a) the throttle should be fully closed.
   - (b) the throttle should be fully open.
   - (c) the throttle should be set at cruise setting.
   - (d) the throttle should be set at flight idle.

   Ref. Ch.7. Para.7.8.

4. When unfeathering a propeller in flight:
   - (a) the r.p.m. lever is set to cruise r.p.m.
   - (b) the r.p.m. lever is set to minimum position.
   - (c) the r.p.m. lever is set to maximum position.
   - (d) the r.p.m. lever is set to flight idle position.

   Ref. Ch.7. Para.7.8.

5. When unfeathering a propeller in flight:
   - (a) select constant speed range prior to selecting unfeather.
   - (b) select constant speed range as soon as the engine has fired.
   - (c) select constant speed range when the engine has warmed up.
   - (d) select constant speed range after selecting unfeather.

   Ref. Ch.7. Para.7.8.

8

ELECTRICALLY OPERATED VARIABLE PITCH PROPELLERS

8.1 Introduction

In some cases, variable pitch propellers may be operated electrically instead of hydraulically, a reversible electric motor being geared by bevel gearing to the root ends of the blades. Such propellers are otherwise similar to the hydraulically operated types.

8.2 Description

Normally the electric motor is situated in the front of the hub and is fitted with a 'no voltage' brake, spring loaded to hold the motor armature from turning except when current is applied.

A reduction gear of very high ratio is interposed between the motor and the blade root ends. It is of the elliptical type and drives a large bevel gear at the rear end.

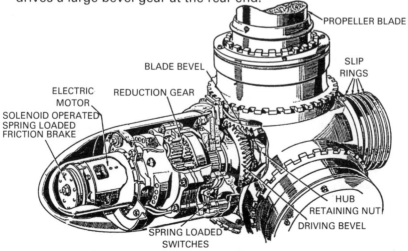

Fig.8-1. Electrically operated propeller.

Fig.8-1 shows an example of the electrically operated variable pitch propeller hub assembly.

The electric current is picked up by four brushes and slip rings at the rear of the hub; the four slip rings are the 'feathering', 'common return', 'fine pitch' and 'coarse pitch' connections.

At the forward ends of the internal connections between slip rings and motor are spring loaded switches which are cut out by cams on the driving wheel, thus acting as pitch range stops. There is also a mechanical fine pitch stop fitted in the reduction gear housing.

8.3 Operation

Electric propellers are usually controlled by an electric governor unit which operates in a similar manner to the normal type as used on hydraulically operated propellers. Instead of the oil pressure passing to the propeller it passes to one side or the other of a servo piston, the movement of which causes current to flow one way or the other to the motor, therefore altering the pitch as required in the same manner as the hydraulically operated type. The variation of pitch is an automatic function when in normal flight in the same way as the hydraulically operated types discussed in previous chapters. However, with an electrically operated propeller often a hand operated control is fitted for emergency use.

8.4 Emergency Hand Operation

A master switch in the cockpit controls all the propeller electric circuits; a three-way switch is used for hand control and an example of its positions and effects are as follows:

(a) Knob to bottom left — blades move to coarser pitch, r.p.m. decreases.

(b) Knob to bottom right — blades go to finer pitch, r.p.m. increases.

(c) Knob upwards — blade pitch automatically controlled by the governor.

In the neutral position the propeller is locked in the pitch it happens to be in. By using (a) or (b) it is possible to select any pitch desired, and lock the propeller in that pitch by returning the knob to neutral or the central position. For feathering purposes a separate switch is fitted.

8.5 Electric Governor Unit

The units uses flyweights, mounted in a cup, to operate a piston valve in a similar way to a normal constant speed unit. There is also a small pressure booster pump and a pressure relief valve.

The controlled oil from the piston valve operates a servo piston which is loaded to the downward position by a spring and engine oil pressure. The servo piston rod carries the positive electrical contact. A cam, driven from the oil pump idler gear, operates a spring loaded rod which carries the fine and coarse pitch contacts. These contacts are arranged above and below the positive contact and are usually referred to as the jogging contacts.

8.6 Operation

When the engine is on speed the controlled oil pressure will hold the servo piston at roughly the centre of its travel, and the jogging contacts will not quite touch the positive contact on either side.

If the engine is overspeeding more high pressure oil will be allowed past the piston valve and the servo piston will rise against its spring. This will cause the positive contacts to touch the coarse pitch contact of the jogging contacts once per revolution of the cam, so coarsening the pitch of the propeller progressively until the engine is again on speed.

Fig.8-2 shows an example electric governor unit.

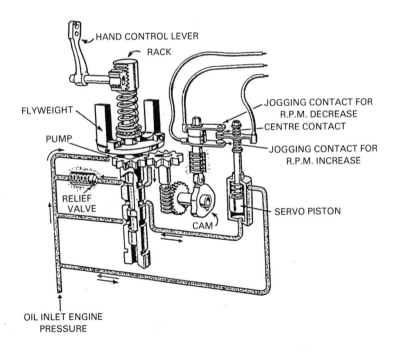

Fig.8-2. Electric propeller governor unit.

If the engine revolutions are too low, the piston valve will cut off the high pressure oil and subject both sides of the servo piston to engine oil pressure. The spring will now force the servo piston to fall. This will now cause the positive contact to touch the fine pitch contact of the jogging contacts once per revolution of the cam until the engine is again on speed.

Note the term 'on speed' in propeller terms means the propeller is rotating at the selected r.p.m. and therefore the engine is rotating at the selected r.p.m.

CHAPTER 8
TEST YOURSELF QUESTIONS

1. An electrically operated variable pitch propeller is operated by:
   (a) an electrically operated hydraulic pump.
   (b) an electric motor connected to each blade to change pitch.
   (c) a single electric motor to collectively change the pitch.
   (d) an electrically signalled hydraulic pitch change mechanism.

   Ref. Ch.8. Para.8.1.

2. The selected pitch of an electrically operated propeller is held in its selected pitch by:
   (a) the pitch change stops.
   (b) a hydraulic brake.
   (c) a spring loaded no voltage brake.
   (d) a mechanical geometric lock.

   Ref. Ch.8. Para.8.2.

3. In the event the electric governor unit fails:
   (a) the propeller will be fixed in the last selected pitch.
   (b) the pitch change may be operated by a manually operated emergency pitch change master switch.
   (c) the propeller will automatically go to fully coarse pitch.
   (d) the propeller will go to flight fine pitch.

   Ref. Ch.8. Para.8.4.

4. The servo piston is:
   (a) hydraulically actuated.
   (b) electrically actuated.
   (c) mechanically actuated.
   (d) actuated by centrifugal force.

   Ref. Ch.8. Para.8.3.

5. The no voltage brake:
   (a) applies a disc brake to the pitch change mechanism.
   (b) applies a mechanical lock to the blade change mechanism.
   (c) is a centrifugal lock.
   (d) holds the armature of the motor.

   Ref. Ch.8. Para.8.2.

9

TURBO-PROPELLERS

9.1 Introduction

A Turbo-Propeller is a propeller which is driven by a gas turbine engine and although the basic propeller theory is the same as for piston engine-driven propellers, there are a number of differences in how constant speed and control are achieved.

9.2 Basic Construction and Operation

Normally the power control lever is connected to both the fuel control unit and the propeller control unit (P.C.U.) in a turbo-propeller installation.

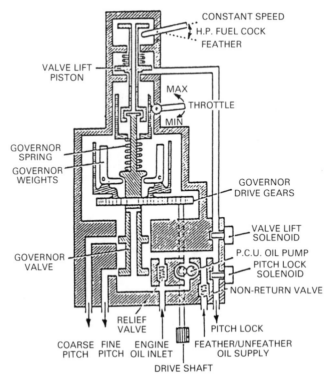

Fig.9-1. Propeller control unit.

Essentially, the pitch change mechanism is similar to the double acting type propeller mechanism in that the constant speed operation is controlled by the governor weights opposing the control spring force to raise or lower the governor valve, and to supply oil the appropriate side of the pitch change piston whenever engine speed varies from the speed selected.

Fig.9-1 illustrates the propeller control unit.

In the on speed condition, centrifugal force on the flyweights balances the force of the control spring, and the governor valve traps oil in both sides of the piston in the pitch change cylinder.

In the underspeed condition, control spring force is greater than the centrifugal force on the flyweights, and the governor valve is lowered, supplying oil to the rear of the pitch change cylinder and providing a drain for oil from the front of the cylinder. Blade angle decreases, and the engine speeds up until centrifugal force on the flyweights balances the force of the control spring, and the governor valve returns to the on speed condition.

In the overspeed condition, control spring force is less than the centrifugal force on the flyweights, and the governor valve is raised, directing oil to the front of the pitch change cylinder and providing a drain for oil in the rear of the cylinder. Blade angle increases, and the engine speed decreases because of the added load, until the flyweights and control spring are again in balance.

Fig.9-2 shows an example double acting pitch change mechanism.

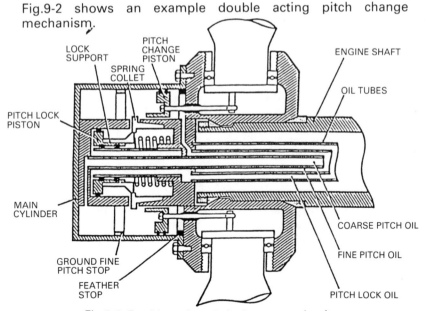

Fig.9-2. Double acting pitch change mechanism.

61

9.3 Feathering

Facilities for the manual feathering of most large propellers are provided both on piston engine types and turbo-props. With some types of turbo-propeller engine installations, however, the drag from a windmilling propeller in fine pitch could be dangerous, in particular with twin-engined aircraft, and to avoid such dangers automatic feathering is also provided.

(a) Manual Feathering

Manual feathering on a piston engine is normally carried out by movement of the r.p.m. control lever to the feather position, and operation of the feathering pump. These actions raise the governor valve, and supply oil under pressure to the appropriate side of pitch change piston. On a turbo-prop installation, manual feathering is carried out by an interconnection between the propeller control unit and the high pressure fuel cock. When the fuel cock is moved to the feather position, linkage to the propeller control unit lifts the governor valve independently of the governor control, and oil is directed to the front of the pitch change piston to turn the blades to fully coarse. Since the oil pump in the propeller control unit is driven by the engine, oil supply pressure may be insufficient to feather the propeller completely, and operation of the electric driven pump is required to boost the pressure.

(b) Automatic Feathering

Automatic feathering is initiated by a torque switch which becomes operational whenever the power levers are set above the idling range.

If engine torque falls below a specific value with the power levers set above idling range, the torque switch closes and completes a circuit to the feathering pump and the valve lift solenoid in the propeller control unit. The solenoid directs oil to the valve lift piston, which in turn lifts the governor valve and opens the oil ports from the feathering pump to the front of the pitch change piston, thus feathering the propeller.

(c) Unfeathering

On turbo-prop installations, when the high pressure fuel cock is open and the power levers closed, the governor valve is in a suitable position to direct oil from the feathering pump to the rear of the pitch change piston. Selection of the feathering pump switch supplies oil to the propeller control unit and then to the propeller, and activates the engine ignition system. When the propeller blades have turned from the feathered position, the airstream starts to rotate the propeller (windmill) and rotate the engine. As the engine is rotated, the oil pumps will again be driven and so the oil pressure starts to build up to complete the unfeathering operation.

(d) Fine Pitch Stops

When starting a turbo-prop engine, as with a piston engine, to ease the load on the powerplant it is necessary to reduce the load on the propeller. This is best achieved by provision by the selection of a very fine pitch on the propeller blades. Whilst this is desired when engine starting, to move into such a fine pitch in flight would be very dangerous, as such a fine pitch in flight could lead to engine overspeeding and excessive drag if the propeller control unit were to fail. To cater for these requirements, the pitch change mechanism for most propellers is provided with two fine pitch stops. The flight fine pitch stop is withdrawn for engine starting and ground operations. The flight fine pitch stop takes the form of spring collet, the prongs of which are designed to spring inwards. When the collet is operating as a stop, the pitch lock piston is held in the forward position by a spring, forcing the spring collet open, and preventing the pitch change piston from moving forward further than the flight fine pitch position. When ground fine pitch is required, a solenoid in the propeller control unit is energised and oil pressure is ducted through a third oil line to the front of the pitch lock piston; as the piston moves rearwards, support for the collet is withdrawn and the prongs spring inwards, allowing the pitch change piston to move fully forward to the ground fine pitch position.

9.4 Reverse Pitch

Reverse pitch is normally used during the landing run to create additional braking force. This is achieved by turning the blades of the propeller from the constant speed range, through ground fine pitch into reverse pitch.

To achieve reverse pitch, the propeller mechanism includes a removable ground fine pitch stop which enables the propeller to fine off to a negative pitch when certain actions have been taken and certain conditions fulfilled.

Various safeguards are incorporated to prevent selection of reverse pitch during flight. The means of achieving negative pitch vary considerably. However, an example of a hydraulically operated propeller is described below:

(a) Electrical control is exercised by throttle mounted switches, weight contact switches that are mounted on the undercarriage, and a master switch or lever to arm the circuit.

With the throttle levers closed beyond normal idling to a datum position, that is, reverse selected, and the weight of the aircraft on its wheels, electrical power is supplied to a pitch stop withdrawal solenoid, and oil pressure is directed to withdraw the fine pitch stop and move the pitch change piston forward to the reverse stop, where it is held by hydraulic pressure. Operation of the reverse lever also changes the sense of operation of the throttle levers, which are pulled further back to increase power in reverse pitch.

(b) Indication of stop withdrawal, and movement of the blades to negative pitch, is provided by hub mounted switches which illuminate appropriate warning lights in the cockpit.

(c) Re-selection of positive blade angle is achieved by moving the throttle into the normal idling range, and by moving the master lever out of the reverse position. Oil is ducted to the front of the pitch change piston, and the blades move to a positive angle; the stop returns to normal operation once the blades have moved past the ground fine pitch angle.

9.5 Beta Control

On some turbo-props, a form of control, known as 'Beta', or blade angle control, is used for ground operations, and may be applied to either a single acting or double acting propeller. With this system, the throttles, usually termed the power levers, operate in a gated quadrant. During flight these levers cannot be closed below the flight idle gate, and the constant speed unit operates normally to maintain the pre-selected propeller speed. In the ground idling and reverse range, the power levers control propeller pitch to vary power at both positive and negative blade angles, at constant propeller speed, and the governor mechanism is overridden. An overspeed sensor, and mechanical pitch stop prevent operation in the ground (fine pitch) range during flight. In the Beta range, the pitch stop is withdrawn, and movement of a power lever rotates a setting cam in the associated constant speed unit, which raises or lowers the governor valve according to whether a coarser or finer pitch is required. A mechanical feed-back mechanism, operated by linkage from the propeller blades, resets the governor valve via a follow-up cam, and pitch change ceases when the angle selected through the power lever is achieved.

CHAPTER 9
TEST YOURSELF QUESTIONS

1. On turbo-prop pitch change mechanisms, the increased oil pressure required to feather the propeller is normally provided by:
   (a) an engine driven booster pump.
   (b) an electrically driven booster pump.
   (c) an accumulator.
   (d) the second stage of the normal oil pump.
   Ref. Ch.9. Para.9.3.

2. Automatic feathering of a turbo-prop is normally available:
   (a) throughout the full pitch range.
   (b) throughout the full 'Beta' range.
   (c) below flight idle only.
   (d) above the idling range.
   Ref. Ch.9. Para.9.3.

3. Automatic feathering of a turbo-prop is initiated by:
   (a) push button control.
   (b) the 'Beta' controller.
   (c) the torque switches.
   (d) the C.S.U.
   Ref. Ch.9. Para.9.3.

4. When unfeathering a turbo-prop:
   (a) the power lever should be in the cruise position.
   (b) the power lever should be in the flight idle position.
   (c) the r.p.m. lever should be in the closed position.
   (d) the power lever should be in the closed position.
   Ref. Ch.9. Para.9.3.

5. On a turbo-prop engine:
   (a) the propeller is feathered by spring pressure.
   (b) the propeller is feathered by counterbalance weights.
   (c) the manual feathering is carried out by an interconnection between the P.C.U. and the H.P. cock.
   (d) the manual feathering is completed by manual force.
   Ref. Ch.9. Para.9.3.

10

PROPELLER INSPECTION AND LIMITATIONS

10.1 Introduction

Whilst it is the engineer's responsibility to maintain and repair the propellers of an aircraft, any damage that may occur to the propeller assembly in normal operational use will first be observed by the pilot. In such circumstances the aircraft may be away from base and the pilot needs to know if the propeller is safe for flight or what limitations may be applied as a result of such damage.

10.2 Limitations of Damage to Blades

The propeller blades are the most likely part of a propeller assembly to sustain damage during ground operations, such as taxying or ground running, and in flight by being struck by foreign objects such as birds, etc.

The following are some of the more common faults that are found on propeller blades:

(a) Tracking

While no visible sign of damage to a propeller blade may be observed, if it has been struck by a foreign object the blade may be bent slightly out of true. This will normally be indicated by vibration from the propeller assembly. In such cases the tracking check of the propeller will show if the blades are out of true.

The track of the blades is the path followed by the blades when the propeller is turned with the aircraft stationary. It is important that each blade shall follow exactly the same track within narrow limits. Correct track may be checked by fixing a pointer just clear of any one blade tip, measuring from this blade, and then turning the propeller until the next blade tip occupies the same position; the measurement should be the same.

Some larger propellers are fitted with a strobe system and tracking should be carried out in accordance with the aircraft manuals.

(b) Hub Retaining Nut

Should the propeller hub retaining nut be disturbed in any way the pilot must note that when it is replaced the correct tightening procedure is used. The correct procedure will be given in the aircraft manuals and different types will vary in the correct procedure. Some details to note:

(i) The propeller retaining nut should not be tightened if the main propeller shaft is warm. Normally after operational use the propeller shaft will become warm and this heat must be allowed to dissipate before the nut is tightened or a tightness check carried out.

(ii) Propeller retaining nuts are normally torque loaded and the degree of loading is very important and must be carried out strictly in accordance with the aircraft manual.

(c) Blade Damage Limitations

The propeller blades should be inspected for damage in the form of abrasions, cuts, nicks, and/or corrosion. Minor erosion or dents may usually be left until the propeller is removed for overhaul. However, cuts or gouges which may lead to cracks, known as stress raisers, should be brought to the notice of the engineer, who will then blend out such damage and repaint the damaged area. The main area of this type of damage is usually on the blade leading edge.

Limitations regarding the area and extent of acceptable damage are laid down by the propeller manufacturer and must be strictly adhered to.

Blades that are bent, twisted outside the normal blade twist profile, or cracked, or have severe surface damage must be considered unserviceable.

(d) Oil Leaks

All connections and joints must be examined for any sign of leaks. Leakage of oil is not acceptable.

(e) Vibration

After the engine has been started and warmed up to normal operating temperature the engine and propeller assemblies should be checked for any sign of excessive vibration. Vibration in a propeller assembly is a clear indication of damage or unserviceability.

CHAPTER 10
TEST YOURSELF QUESTIONS

1. The track of the propeller blades is the:
    (a) path followed by the blades when the aircraft is in flight.
    (b) path followed by the blades when the engine is at reference revolutions.
    (c) path followed by the blades when the aircraft is stationary and the propeller turned by hand.
    (d) path followed by the blades when the aircraft is on the ground and the engine at idle r.p.m.

    Ref. Ch.10. Para.10.2.

2. Tracking checks are carried out by measuring relative points at the:
    (a) roots of the blades.
    (b) tips of the blades.
    (c) span of each blade.
    (d) hub of each blade.

    Ref. Ch.10. Para.10.2.

3. Dents to the leading edge of a propeller blade:
    (a) are not acceptable.
    (b) are usually acceptable until the next propeller overhaul.
    (c) may be ignored.
    (d) may be repaired immediately by painting over them.

    Ref. Ch.10. Para.10.2.

4. Propeller retaining nuts:
    (a) must only be hand tightened to allow for expansion.
    (b) must be tightened when the shaft is heated.
    (c) must not be tightened when the shaft is warm.
    (d) must be tightened before each flight.

    Ref. Ch.10. Para.10.2.

5. Propeller assemblies:
    (a) are checked for vibration before flight.
    (b) must be continually monitored for vibration in flight.
    (c) must be continually monitored for vibration when in operation.
    (d) are checked for vibration before and after flight.

Ref. Ch.10. Para.10.2.

11

PROPELLER DE-ICING

11.1 Introduction

Ice in the atmosphere is caused by coldness acting on moisture in the air. Icing consists of crystals, their size and density being dependent on the temperature and the type of water from which they form. Ice formation on propellers can be classified under three main headings: Glaze Ice, Rime Ice and Hoar Frost.

11.2 Glaze Ice

Ice forms when the aircraft propeller encounters large water drops, in cloud or in rain, and both the air and the propeller are below freezing point. The liquid flows over the propeller blade surfaces before freezing and so the ice formed is dense, tough and adheres closely to the surface of the blade material. Glaze ice is the most severe and dangerous form of ice formation.

11.3 Rime Ice

This type of ice formation is a light, porous, opaque, rough deposit and results from small water drops freezing as individual particles with little or no spreading, when the air and propeller are below freezing point.

11.4 Hoar Frost

This type of ice is formed in clear air when water vapour is converted directly into ice and builds up a white feathery semi-crystalline coating, when the propeller is below freezing point.

11.5 Effects of Ice

The effects of ice formation on propellers are a danger to propeller performance and safety, in that:

(a) Changes of blade section resulting in reduced thrust.

(b) Roughening of the blade surfaces resulting in increased drag.

(c) Weight of the ice will increase loading and upset stability.

(d) Ice formation may upset pitch change movement of the propeller blades.

(e) Ice formation on propellers may cause vibration, loss of efficiency, and if dislodged can cause severe damage or be ingested by the engine.

11.6 De-icing System Types

There are two basic types of de-icing system used on propeller assemblies. They are de-icing fluid systems and electrically de-icing systems.

11.7 Fluid De-icing Systems

The system provides a film of de-icing fluid to the propeller blade surface during flight, which mixes with the water, or moisture, on the propeller blades, reducing the freezing point of the mixture. Where ice has already formed on the blades, the fluid penetrates under the ice, which then loosens it, and the ice is then thrown off by centrifugal force.

Ice tends to form more readily at the root end of the propeller blades and it is at this point that the de-icing fluid is fed on to the blades surfaces by what are termed 'Slinger Rings'. The slinger rings are fed with de-icing fluid from a reservoir or tank which on leaving the tank passes through a filter and is then delivered under pressure to the slinger rings, mounted in the hub of the propeller. The de-icing fluid is pumped to the slinger rings by an electrically driven pump. The pump is controlled from the cockpit by a three-position switch which may be selected in one of the three modes of 'Automatic', 'Manual' or 'Emergency'.

(a) Manual Selection

Low flow rate pump runs intermittently at a ratio of one period 'On' to four 'Off'.

(b) Automatic

Flow as manual selection but operation is controlled by ice detectors.

(c) Emergency

This switch is gated to prevent inadvertent operation. High flow rate with pump running continuously to combat severe icing conditions.

Two indicator lights are normally provided: a green light to indicate the pump is running and a red light to indicate emergency is selected.

11.8 Overshoes

At the root end of the propeller blade on some aircraft types, particularly propellers fitted to larger types of aircraft, are devices known as overshoes. The overshoe is bonded to the leading edge of the blade and extends for about twenty-five per cent of the blade length towards the tip. Its purpose is to provide a guide to produce an even spread of de-icing fluid across the propeller blade.

11.9 Electrical De-Icing Systems

The principle of the electrical de-icing system is to provide effective de-icing by heat generated within heater elements constructed from resistance wire to form a mat type structure which is in turn bonded to the leading edge of the propeller. The heater element is supplied with a.c. or d.c. electrica power, depending on type. Most modern systems utilize single phase a.c. electricity. On many modern turbo-prop aircraft, the propeller de-icing system is integrated with the powerplant de-icing system.

The power required for the heating elements is conveyed via cables, slip rings, and by brushes contained within a brush block housing. The slip rings are mounted at the rear of the propeller hub, or on a starter ring gear, and the brush housing on the engine front case. However, in some systems the method of mounting may be the reverse way round. The cables are of sufficient length and are positioned so as to allow for movement of the blades through their complete pitch range.

11.10 Heating Control

Efficient operation of these types of electrical de-icing requires a relatively high consumption of electrical power. This is, however, controlled by employing a cyclic de-icing technique whereby a short unheated period allows a thin film of ice to build up on the leading edges of the propeller blades. Before this film of ice builds up sufficiently to interfere appreciably with the aerodynamic characteristics of the blades, the cyclic control applies heating power. The ice already deposited then acts as a thermal insulation, and as the ice in contact with the blade melts, the main ice catch is carried away under the action of centrifugal and aerodynamic force.

12

PERFORMANCE AND DESIGN

12.1 Introduction

This chapter deals with some of the variations and specialist features in propeller design and the general handling and performance of propeller driven aircraft. Each aircraft type has its own handling features and must be learned on type. The following paragraphs draw to your attention some general aspects of the behaviour of propeller driven aircraft.

12.2 Counter Rotating Propellers

This type of propeller is sometimes used on high powered engines to more efficiently transform the power of the engine into useful thrust; this is effected by mounting two separate propellers in line on two shafts, one inside the other which rotate the propellers in opposite directions, one clockwise the other anti-clockwise. The two propellers rotating in opposite directions will cancel out the torque effects and therefore improve some handling characteristics of the aircraft. A further improvement is obtained because the slipstream is straighter than that behind a single propeller.

Usually the front propeller contains the pitch change mechanism and alterations to the rear propeller pitch are transmitted by a translation unit. The propeller has normal constant speed operation and is handled in a similar manner to other single propellers.

Note: The term Counter Rotating Propellers is normally used when each propeller shaft is driven by a separate engine or powerplant. This term may also be used to, for example, describe the action of the rotational direction on a twin engined aircraft where the engines are mounted one in each wing, one with a left handed propeller the other with a right handed propeller.

12.3 Contra-Rotating Propellers

At first sight the contra-rotating propeller appears to be the same as a counter rotating propeller. However, the accepted definition of the contra-rotating propeller is the mounting of two propellers in line, driven by a single engine and caused to rotate in opposite directions by a gearbox mounted at the front of the engine. It has similar advantages to the counter rotating arrangement. With this type it is not possible to feather just one element of a twin in line propeller.

12.4 Braking Propellers

Some propellers, in addition to their constant speed variable pitch capabilities, have reversible pitch. The propeller pitch can be reversed quickly through zero pitch so enabling the propeller to exert a reverse thrust, or braking force. These propellers are used to produce reverse thrust immediately after touch down as an aid to reducing the length of the landing run and to assist in manoeuvring during taxying.

Full throttle, in most cases, can be applied when the angle of the blade is in reverse pitch, allowing maximum power to be available for braking purposes. The constant speed unit is inoperative when reverse pitch is engaged and R.P.M. will therefore be controlled by throttle movement.

12.5 Handling

(a) Failure of the Constant Speed Unit.

If the C.S.U. fails in flight, the pitch may lock at the setting which was being maintained at the time of the failure. If failure occurs during a climb, the R.P.M. at the time of the failure may be high for continuous flight. The R.P.M. should be kept as low as possible by restricting the throttle openings and by flying at a suitably reduced airspeed.

(b) Failure of C.S.U. in Level Flight

If failure occurs in level flight in the cruise, the R.P.M. will normally be low and the propeller pitch at a fairly coarse setting. These conditions will be suitable for level flight. However, any manoeuvre requiring high power should be avoided.

(c) Probable Cause of C.S.U. Failure

Dirt or grit in the oil is the most likely cause of C.S.U. failure. Whilst every effort is taken to avoid contamination of the oil, particles worn from the components in the system will cause possible problems and failure of C.S.U. operation. When a problem is indicated the first action that should be taken is to exercise the C.S.U. in an attempt to dislodge the foreign matter causing the problem by allowing the oil to circulate through the C.S.U. The oil will be caused to flow by operating the R.P.M. indicator. Complete failure may be caused through loss of oil pressure due to a fractured pipeline or leaking seal. This may eventually lead to a complete loss of engine oil and so under such circumstances, if possible, the propeller should be feathered immediately.

(d) Flying at Low Temperatures

Under cold weather conditions, the oil in the C.S.U. may congeal and make C.S.U. operation very sluggish. In such circumstances the R.P.M. lever should be operated from time to time to circulate the oil in the C.S.U. and maintain a free flow.

(e) Electric Propellers

Electric Propellers are equipped with an alternative manual control. In the event of a C.S.U. failure, pitch change can still be maintained through manual selection.

(f) Overspeeding

Overspeeding is often caused by a complete loss of oil pressure or possibly the failure of the C.S.U. In either situation, the following actions should be taken immediately to prevent serious damage to the engine.

(i)   Reduce the airspeed.

(ii) Close the throttle.

(iii) If the propeller cannot be returned to constant speed conditions, attempt to feather.

If the propeller will not feather and the aircraft will not maintain height due to the high drag caused by the propeller, the throttle may be opened slightly, with caution, in an attempt to obtain a small amount of power and so reduce the drag. R.P.M. must not exceed normal take off maximum.

12.6   Failure to Feather

If the propeller fails to feather when selected, using the correct procedure, with electric and certain hydraulic types an alternative method may be used. Normally this will cause the propeller to feather, but at a greatly reduced rate:

(a) Electric Variable Pitch Propeller
The switch should be held to the 'decrease' R.P.M. position until the propeller stops.

(b) Hydraulically Operated Variable Pitch Propellers

On types which the R.P.M. control lever has a feathering gate, the lever should be moved back through the gate.

It should be noted that the drag on a windmilling propeller

in fine pitch is much greater than the drag on a feathered propeller. Flight with asymmetric power will be adversely affected and critical speeds will be higher.

12.7 Turbo-prop Engine Handling

The following is related to the effects on the propeller and not specifically to the gas turbine element of the powerplant.

(a) Take-off

When the aircraft is correctly aligned on the runway, the brakes should be applied and the R.P.M. increased to the recommended value for the particular aircraft type. When any increase or decrease of R.P.M. is required, any throttle lever movement should be made as smoothly and as slowly as possible. On releasing brakes for take-off, smoothly increase the power. If smooth operation of the throttle or power lever is not exercised, overspeeding of the propeller may occur. The maximum torque may be reduced as altitude or air temperature increases.

(b) Flight

In normal flight conditions the throttle should not be closed below the flight idle position except in a re-light situation. When the engine is operating within the constant speed range, all movements of the throttle between the flight idle gate and the take-off gate should be made smoothly. There is a possibility of a flame-out if the throttle is closed too quickly. The R.P.M. should not be allowed to fall below the constant speed range. If, however, this does happen, the propeller fines off until it reaches the flight fine pitch stops. If this occurs, the stops should be disengaged otherwise the propeller will behave as a fixed pitch propeller, that is to say, any further reduction in power will result in a reduction in R.P.M. and any rapid opening of the throttle may stall the engine. Normal R.P.M. can be maintained by observing the indicated airspeed and power combinations for the particular aircraft. When it is not practical to meet these conditions, the flight fine pitch stops should be withdrawn manually or by lowering the undercarriage.

(c) Engine Failure

When a piston engine fails in flight, or on the ground when taxying, taking off or landing, the C.S.U. moves the propeller pitch to fully fine, usually an angle of about 25 degrees, in an attempt to maintain the set R.P.M., after which the propeller windmills until it is feathered.

With turbo-prop engines, however, an engine failure would result in the propeller pitch reducing to a much smaller or finer angle, sometimes as low as 12 to 8 degrees, a suitable angle for engine starting. The much smaller angle of pitch causes the blades to present the maximum frontal area to the airflow, resulting in very high drag and a steep gliding angle. The airflow over the tailplane, fin and rudder will be disrupted to such an extent that rudder and elevator control will be seriously impaired. The propeller is said to be 'Discing' when this occurs. To prevent this undesired situation developing, a Reverse Torque Switch is fitted to many aircraft which, when activated by an overspeeding propeller, i.e. torque conditions are reversed, the switch overrides the C.S.U. and causes the feathering motor to feather the propeller. Sometimes a momentary period of reverse torque may be encountered, which may occur when throttling back too quickly, which will be indicated by the flashing of the reverse torque warning light. However, when pitch adjusts itself after a matter of seconds the feathering action is halted and the propeller reverts back to normal operation.

Note: On turbo-prop powered aircraft it is usual for the flight fine pitch stops to be withdrawn automatically when the undercarriage is selected down to enable the pitch to operate below flight fine for taxying and engine starting purposes.

(d) Approach and Landing

Turbo-prop engines, in comparison with pure turbo-jet engines, have poor response to inputs when on approach. As a result, early corrective action must be taken when undershooting. When an increase of power is selected, for example, there is no immediate impression of an increase of power from the engine, and so reference should be made to the torque meter to gauge the engine response. The throttle should never be closed behind the flight idle gate until the aircraft has touched down on the runway. After touchdown, deceleration is very poor if the throttle is left at the flight idle position or gate. This is primarily due to the high residual thrust that will still be produced. The throttles should be moved to the ground idle position on touch down. Rapid closing of the throttle to the ground idle position should be avoided as this will cause a rapid fining off of the propeller with a sudden large increase of drag. Whilst this will produce rapid deceleration in the initial stages of the landing run, the discing effect of the very fine pitch is to blank the rudder and elevator, greatly reducing their effectiveness. As a result, any drift or yaw at this stage will be accentuated and any swing which may develop will require very careful and early use of the brakes. The throttle should therefore be closed smoothly, thereby avoiding such situations. The use of power to check swings is not particularly effective due to the poor response of the turbo-prop.

(e) Stopping Turbo-prop Engines

The engine should be run down at the specified R.P.M. to ensure even cooling and the throttle closed to the ground idle position. The engine is stopped by closing the H.P. Cock fully. Some engines require the start pitch button to be pressed to speed up the feathering of the propeller to slow it down more quickly and, where fitted, the propeller brake applied. Most turbo-props are feathered when parked and a brake is also provided to prevent the propeller windmilling.

12.8   Turbo-prop Synchronizing of Propellers

The primary purpose of synchronizing propellers, both in flight and where possible on the ground, is to reduce noise levels. Synchronizing ensures that the propeller speeds, on multi-engined aircraft, are all the same. The synchronizing system utilizes an electrical system which compares electrical signals from engine mounted generators. One engine is designated as the master engine and any out of balance signals from the other engines are automatically corrected by electrically trimming the engine speed until all signals are in phase.

12.9   Turbo-prop Synchrophasing of Propellers

The synchrophasing system also assists in reducing noise levels and in principle ensures that any given propeller blade of a propeller is in the same relative position as the corresponding blade of the propeller on the master engine. This is achieved automatically by very fine trimming of the engine speeds as a result of signals transmitted from the engine's synchrophasing generators.

12.10   Propeller Slipstream Effect

In the same way as the aircraft's aerofoils, such as the wing and tailplane, provide their lift by deflecting the air downwards, the propeller through a similar action produces thrust by forcing air backwards. The result of this action is a stream of air which flows over the fuselage, wings or mainplanes, tailplane and fin, this stream of air is called the slipstream. The slipstream generally maintains a flow of air behind the propeller approximately equal to the diameter of the propeller, and with the exception of an area a short distance behind the propeller itself, where the diameter of the slipstream contracts slightly, the same diameter is maintained for some considerable distance, usually well in excess of the length of the aircraft. Fig.12-1 shows the slipstream flow over the aircraft.

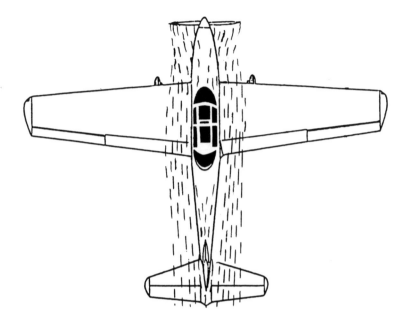

Fig.12-1. Propeller slipstream.

The slipstream velocity is usually greater than that of the aircraft airspeed. Under some conditions the slipstream velocity may be as much as 100 per cent to 120 per cent higher at the aircraft's stalling speed. It should be noted therefore, that the slipstream flowing over various parts of the aircraft may be at twice the velocity of the airflow flowing over other parts of the aircraft effectively outside the slipstream effect.

Within the slipstream effect the drag will be four times as great as the drag outside the effects of the slipstream. As forward speed is increased the difference is not so great, being only about fifty per cent at normal speeds, and as little as ten per cent at high speeds.

The extra velocity generated by the slipstream may be advantageous in providing more effective control for rudder and elevators especially when the aircraft is moving at low airspeeds. This is basically the same as the wing blowing and jet flap principles by maintaining laminar flow over the surfaces and therefore minimizing boundary layer separation. This is normally only available with propeller driven aircraft. As well as increasing the effective control over the rudder and elevators, the slipstream will provide increased effectiveness of flaps by blowing air over the wing and flap surfaces and therefore again reducing the boundary layer separation problem.

In addition to the increased velocity of the propeller slipstream, the propeller also imparts a swirl effect, or rotary motion to the flow of the slipstream which rotates in the same direction as the propeller. This creates a tendency for the airflow to strike the one side of the keel surface and/or fin more effectively than the other, and as a consequence may have a considerable effect on the directional and lateral balance of the aircraft. See Fig.12-2.

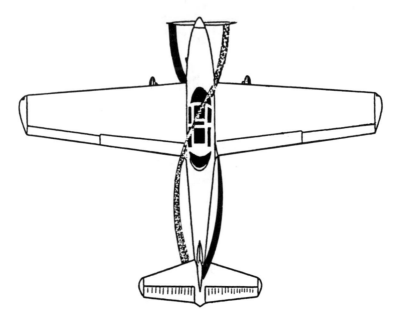

Fig.12-2. Airflow pattern due to rotational effect of the propeller.

If these effects are compensated for in normal flight, by offsetting the fin so that it does not lie directly for and aft, then the balance will be upset when the engine/propeller reduces r.p.m., or stops, and the slipstream ceases to exert its influences.

This particular set of problems is usually satisfied only in part on most aircraft from a design point of view. It is virtually impossible to remove all such disadvantageous problems from an aircraft and so a compromise is settled upon, which generally satisfies most conditions.

12.11 Gyroscopic Effect

In addition to that discussed in previous chapters the gyroscopic effect is dealt with here as an operational, or performance problem. The modern propeller assembly constitutes a considerable rotating mass which may cause a gyroscopic effect. Whilst every effort is made to reduce the weight of the propeller assembly some form of gyroscopic effect cannot totally be avoided. A rotating body tends to resist any change in its plane of rotation, and if such a change does take place there is a superimposed tendency for the plane of rotation to change also in a direction at right angles to that in which it is forced. This can be illustrated with a wheel mounted on a shaft. If the wheel is rapidly rotated and is held by the horizontal shaft and the holder attempts to keep the shaft horizontal while he turns, the shaft will either tilt upwards or downwards, depending on whether the holder turns with the direction of rotation of the wheel, or in the opposite direction. An aircraft will behave in much the same way in that, if the aircraft has a right handed propeller, that is a propeller which rotates clockwise when viewed from the cockpit, the nose will tend to drop, or if the aircraft is equipped with a left handed propeller the tail will drop, i.e. the nose will tend to pitch up.

This tendency is normally only appreciated in exceptional cases, normally on aircraft fitted with very large propellers or on some very old aircraft designs which used rotary engines where the rotating mass is much greater.

12.12 Swing on Take-Off

Many aircraft designs have a tendency to swing on take-off to one side, i.e. a yawing action to port or starboard. There are many possible reasons for this tendency on some aircraft some of the basic principles of which have been discussed earlier in this book.

There are a number of possibilities that should be examined. First, the main probable cause is the propeller, in that the torque reaction of the propeller on a right handed type will cause the reaction to be anti-clockwise, this in turn will cause the left hand wheel to be forced more firmly on the ground creating greater friction which in turn should cause the aircraft to yaw to port.

The second point that should be considered is the effect of the slipstream.

Assuming the same right handed propeller, rotating clockwise as viewed from the cockpit, it will also create a clockwise rotating slipstream which will have the effect of striking the fin and rudder on the left hand, or port side. This will cause the aircraft to yaw to the left as the fin and rudder will be forced to the right which causes the aircraft to move about the normal or vertical axis.

A further problem that must be considered by the pilot when handling tail wheeled aircraft is that when the tail wheel is on the ground and the propeller axis is inclined upwards with the aircraft travelling along the ground, or runway, the down going propeller blade will strike the air at a larger angle of attack than the upgoing blade, the result of which is an increase of thrust on the down going blade and therefore in the case of a right handed propeller again will cause the aircraft to yaw to the left, as there is more thrust produced to the right of the centre line than the left.

By fitting contra-rotating propellers virtually all the problems of asymmetrical slipstream, propeller torque, and gyroscopic action are removed. The use of such propeller assemblies increases cost, is heavier than normal or single propeller assemblies, and tend to be far more complex. The contra rotating propeller provides a straight high speed flow over the wings and tailplane providing improved control and stability.

Fig.12-3 illustrates a contra-rotating propeller assembly.

Fig.12-3. Contra-rotating propeller.

12.13 Propeller Effects on Nose Wheeled Aircraft

On aircraft equipped with nose wheeled undercarriage assemblies there is inherent directional stability when in motion on the ground due to the fact the C of G is ahead of the main wheels, unlike the tailwheel configuration which suffers from divergent tendencies.

A nose wheeled aircraft is virtually in its normal flying attitude throughout its take-off run. Asymmetric blade effect and gyroscopic effect can be almost ignored. The nose wheel configuration is however, still subject to torque reaction, slipstream effect, and cross winds, the swing on take-off is, never the less, more easily controlled.

12.14   The Modern Propeller

At subsonic speeds the propeller offers greater efficiency than the turbojet engine when operating at low and medium altitudes. This efficiency can be used to produce more thrust from a given engine size, or fuel economy by using a small engine with a lower fuel consumption.

To extend the use of the turboprop engine into the higher speed and altitude ranges, that is speeds of up to Mach 0.8 and a cruise capability at 30,000 ft, requires the development of advanced propeller designs.

Fig. 12-4. Modern turboprop propeller.

83

As the propeller blade is essentially an aerofoil section, by applying existing high speed flight techniques to the design of the propeller blades, it is possible to delay the onset of compressibility effects at the outboard sections of the propeller blades, i.e. to delay the Critical Mach Number (Mcrit). Such modern techniques involve the use of reduced blade thickness, using improved aerofoil sections and propeller blade tip sweep.

Fig.12-4 shows an example of such a modern propeller.

The development of the modern propeller can be attributed to two main basic requirements. The first requirement being to produce a more economic use of the gas turbine engine, and the second to reduce the noise generated by the complete power plant.

Economy is an essential requirement for today's civil aircraft operator and so engine manufacturers have spent large sums of money on research to achieve more economic standards. This has lead to the development of two distinct types of engine, the first being the widely used Turbo-Fan type gas turbine engine. The Turbo-Fan engine is essentially a High By-pass gas turbine engine producing a by-pass ratio in the order of 5:1 leading to a very high by-pass ratio of 15:1. During the 1980s it became clear

Fig.12-5. Prop-fan.

that in order to reduce the fuel bills and reduce the size of the engine required for a given task the greater use of improved propellers was essential. This has lead in certain areas to the use of the Prop-Fan engine, that is a modern propeller development of the Turbo-prop engine. At the same time increased efficiency was being obtained from the Turbo-Fan developments and so the High By-Pass engine was a natural progression by shrouding the Front Fan, or low pressure compressor. This has produced a more economic engine and one which makes far less noise due to reduced blade tip turbulence. A further progression is the development of the Unducted Fan which is only possible because of the great strides which have been made in propeller technology. Fig.12-5 shows an example of a Prop Fan.

12.15 Summary of Propeller Development Types

(a) Modern Prop-Fan Engine.

Engines on which this type of propeller are used are developing in excess of 12,000 hp providing high thrust with low noise and increased economy. In order to provide high thrust, at low velocity to minimize noise, at least eight blades are normally fitted. Sweeping of the blades delays Mcrit and reduces the noise from the tips of the blades. The sweep also alters the phase of the noise generated by each radial section along the blade causing a certain amount of interference which results in noise reduction.

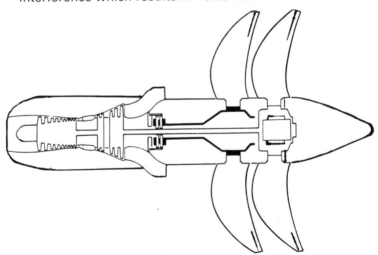

Fig.12-6. Prop-fan engine.

(b) Low and High By-Pass Engines.

The development of this engine type has taken two forms,

either by having the fan at the front or the rear. In both cases the fan element by-passes air around the engine core in the order of 1:1 for a low by-pass type, that is equal parts of air enter the engine core and an equal amount of air by-passes the engine. The air that by-passes the engine core may be ducted the full length of the engine, or partially ducted for only part of the length of the engine. The high by-pass engine produces a by-pass ratio of 5:1, that is for every part of air entering the engine core, five parts by-pass the engine core.

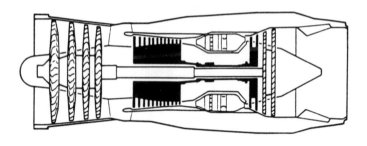

Fig.12-7. Low by-pass ducted fan engine.

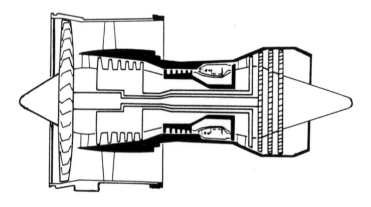

Fig.12-8. High by-pass partially ducted fan (front fan engine)

It must be noted the examples given are just examples as almost any combination of the arrangements of these engines can, and have been used.

(c) Very High By-Pass Engines.

The by-pass ratio of this category of engine is in the region of 15:1. Fig.12-9 shows an example.

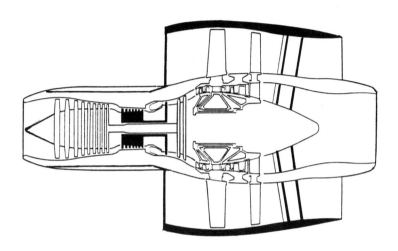

Fig.12-9. Very high by-pass engine.

As can be seen the fan portion, or element of these engines can be considered as being a form of propeller and may be used in the same way as earlier propellers to provide reverse thrust for braking by reversing the pitch of the blades. In this type of configuration this is known as "Cold" reverse thrust as opposed to "Hot" reverse thrust which is provided by the hot exhaust gases of the engine. Cold reverse thrust is provided by reversing the pitch of the fan element only.

12.16 Advanced Propellers or Ultra High By-Pass

A further advance of the propeller is the total replacement of the "Fan" concept by a propeller assembly. Unlike the turboprop design where the turbine assembly is utilised to drive a propeller via a gearbox, in this type the propeller forms an extension of the turbine assembly itself. This can be best seen in Figs.12-10 and 12-11. This latest design achieved a by-pass ratio in the order of 30:1 and higher. It is proving to be very economical and is much quieter. It may take the form of a single or contra-rotating propeller assembly.

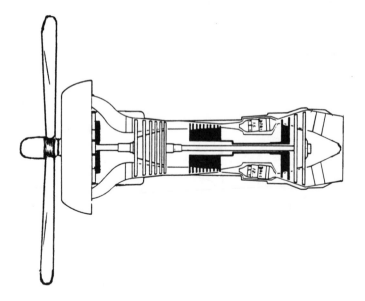

Fig.12-10. Turboprop with propeller driven by rear turbine.

Fig.12-11. Advanced propeller concept.

12.17 Propeller Spinners

The performance of the propeller is not only to provide thrust to support the aircraft in forward flight. The airflow produced by the propeller assembly must be as turbulent free as possible, not only to ensure a smooth slipstream is produced but also to provide, in the case of piston engined aircraft, a smooth flow of air to cool the engine. Also in the case of the turboprop engine an airflow to the engine intake to supply the compressor with air. To assist in the direction of the smooth airflow a spinner is normally fitted over the hub of the propeller, the spinner reduces drag and assists in the direction of the slipstream to the compressor, or cooling intake.

An example of a spinner is shown in Fig.12-12.

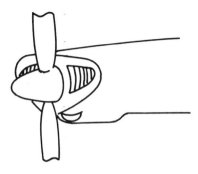

Fig.12-12. The spinner.

12.18 Propeller Contamination

It is of the utmost importance that the propeller is carefully examined before every flight. It should be checked for security of attachment, including the spinner, signs of excessive erosion, cracking, stone damage, and contamination. On some types of wooden propeller checks should also be made for any signs of delamination, that is to ensure the layers of wood from which the propeller is manufactured, are not separating in any way. It is also very important with this type of construction that contamination is avoided. Contamination from oil in the atmosphere may attack the bonding material, or glue, which is used during manufacture to hold the layers of wood together, causing delamination. To prevent this the propeller blades should be cleaned at regular intervals to remove any build up of contaminants.

Note:– DO NOT HANDLE PROPELLERS as they may be "LIVE". Before carrying out cleaning ensure the propeller and engine ignition system are made safe.

CHAPTER 12
TEST YOURSELF QUESTIONS

1. When flying in low temperature conditions:
    (a) the C.S.U. is heated to prevent congealing of the oil.
    (b) the C.S.U. operation should be kept to a minimum.
    (c) the C.S.U. should be exercised periodically to prevent the oil congealing.
    (d) the C.S.U. r.p.m. lever should be set to a higher value.
    Ref. Ch.12. Para.12.5.

2. Overspeeding of the propeller in flight may be the result of:
    (a) excessive oil pressure in the C.S.U.
    (b) loss of oil pressure in the C.S.U.
    (c) faulty latches.
    (d) r.p.m. lever set too high.
    Ref. Ch.12. Para.12.5.

3. On turbo-prop aircraft it is normal for:
    (a) the flight fine pitch stops to withdraw when the undercarriage is selected down.
    (b) the flight fine pitch stops to withdraw when the weight on switches are activated.
    (c) the flight fine pitch stops to engage when the weight is on the undercarriage.
    (d) the flight line pitch stops to be unaffected by undercarriage operation.
    Ref. Ch.12. Para.12.7.

4. Operation of the reverse torque switch:
    (a) feathers the propeller.
    (b) overrides the C.S.U.
    (c) overrides the throttle.
    (d) unfeathers the propeller.
    Ref. Ch.12. Para.12.7.

5. Synchronizing of propellers is based on:
    (a) all propellers are set at the same pitch angle.

(b) all propellers rotate at the same speed.

(c) all propellers develop the same thrust.

(d) all propellers develop the same shaft horsepower.

Ref. Ch.12. Para.12.8.

FINAL PRACTICE QUESTIONS

PROPELLERS

1. When unfeathering some types of turbo-prop, this is achieved by:
   - (a) pushing the r.p.m. lever fully forward.
   - (b) pulling the r.p.m. lever fully back.
   - (c) pulling the throttle fully back.
   - (d) moving the H.P. fuel cock to the feather position.

   Ref. Ch.9. Para.9.3.

2. When unfeathering a turbo-prop:
   - (a) the power levers are closed.
   - (b) the r.p.m. levers are closed.
   - (c) the H.P. fuel cock is closed.
   - (d) the throttle must be set to cruise.

   Ref. Ch.9. Para.9.3.

3. Automatic feathering of a turbo-prop is initiated by:
   - (a) a torque switch.
   - (b) the power levers being set at idling r.p.m.
   - (c) the centrifugal clutch.
   - (d) the manual feathering override switch.

   Ref. Ch.9. Para.9.3.

4. When a turbo-prop moves into negative pitch:
   - (a) hub mounted switches operate warning lights in the cockpit.
   - (b) the blade thrust face is facing forward.
   - (c) the stops will engage.
   - (d) the blade pressure face will face aft.

   Ref. Ch.9. Para.9.3.

5. Beta control:
   - (a) will automatically feather the blades in flight, when selected.

(b) will operate on the ground only by manual selection.

(c) will operate only below flight idle.

(d) can be operated under any conditions of flight.

Ref. Ch.9. Para.9.3.

6. When a piston-engined V.P. Propeller is to be feathered:

(a) the ignition of the engine should be switched off first.

(b) the throttle of the engine should be fully closed first.

(c) the feathering switch should be first operated.

(d) the fuel supply should be turned off first.

Ref. Ch.7. Para.7.5.

7. The geometric pitch of a propeller in flight is:

(a) equal to the blade angle plus slip.

(b) greater than the slip plus effective pitch.

(c) greater than effective pitch.

(d) less than effective pitch.

Ref. Ch.1. Para.1.3.

8. In flight, the propeller total reaction is:

(a) aft of the pitch change axis.

(b) acts through the pitch change axis.

(c) acts through the blade C of G.

(d) forward of the pitch change axis.

Ref. Ch.1. Para.1.4.

9. A left-handed propeller will:

(a) rotate clockwise when viewed from the cockpit.

(b) rotate clockwise when viewed from the front of the aircraft.

(c) rotate anti-clockwise when viewed from the front of the aircraft.

(d) be fitted to the port engine.

Ref. Ch.1. Para.1.7.

10. The angle of advance of a propeller is:
    (a) the same as the helix angle.
    (b) the same as the blade angle.
    (c) the angle of attack plus the helix angle.
    (d) the same as the angle of attack.

Ref. Ch.1. Para.1.8.

11. A propeller's ability to absorb power may be improved by:
    (a) decrease the solidity.
    (b) increase the solidity.
    (c) decrease the diameter.
    (d) decrease the blade chord.

Ref. Ch.1. Para.1.8J.

12. A constant speed propeller:
    (a) is controlled by controlling engine r.p.m.
    (b) maintains the engine at constant r.p.m.
    (c) maintains constant speed by adjusting the engine C.S.U.
    (d) maintains constant propeller thrust.

Ref. Ch.2. Para.2.4.

13. Selection of a specific engine r.p.m., with a constant speed propeller fitted, is achieved by:
    (a) the engine throttle adjustment.
    (b) the engine r.p.m. lever adjustment.
    (c) the propeller r.p.m. adjustment.
    (d) the propeller thrust adjustment.

Ref. Ch.5. Para.5.1.

14. Engine r.p.m. is adjusted in flight on a piston-engined aircraft with a constant speed propeller by:
    (a) adjustment of the engine throttle.
    (b) adjustment of the r.p.m. lever which adjusts the governor spring.
    (c) adjustment of the r.p.m. lever which directly adjusts blade pitch.
    (d) adjustment of the throttle which adjusts the C.S.H. spring.

Ref. Ch.5. Para.5.3.

15. A double-acting propeller:
    (a) utilizes oil to operate the pitch change piston in both directions.
    (b) utilizes oil to operate the pitch change piston in one direction.
    (c) is a propeller which has a two position pitch variation capability.
    (d) is a propeller which has an aerodynamic braking capability.

    Ref. Ch.6. Para.6.1.

16. Normally an electrically operated variable pitch propeller assembly is controlled by:
    (a) a hydraulically controlled mechanism.
    (b) an electrically controlled mechanism.
    (c) a hydro/mechanical mechanism.
    (d) an electrical/mechanically operated mechanism.

    Ref. Ch.8. Para.8.3.

17. The governor of an electrically operated variable pitch propeller is:
    (a) similar to a normal C.S.U. governor.
    (b) purely electrically controlled.
    (c) hydraulically controlled.
    (d) a hydro/electrical device.

    Ref. Ch.8. Para.8.5.

18. On an electrically operated variable pitch propeller, when a specific blade pitch has been reached, the blade is locked in that position by:
    (a) a hydraulic brake.
    (b) a mechanical friction brake.
    (c) a no voltage brake.
    (d) an electrically actuated piston.

    Ref. Ch.8. Para.8.2.

19. The tracking of a propeller is carried out:
    (a) measuring the distance between each blade tip.

(b) by measuring relative points at the blade tip against a fixed point when slowly rotating the propeller.

(c) by measuring relative points at the blade root against a fixed point when slowly rotating the propeller.

(d) by measuring the span of each blade.

Ref. Ch.10. Para.10.2.

20. Propeller assemblies:
    (a) are checked for vibration before and after flight.
    (b) must be continually monitored for vibration when in operation.
    (c) must be only tightened to grip the hub, so allowing for expansion.
    (d) are lifed to a certain number of calendar days.

Ref. Ch.10. Para.10.2.

21. On some single acting propellers, the blades are:
    (a) assisted in moving into coarse pitch by counterweights.
    (b) assisted in moving into the feathered position by counterweights.
    (c) assisted in moving out of coarse pitch by counterweights.
    (d) assisted in moving into fully fine pitch by counterweights.

Ref. Ch.4. Para.4.2.

22. Reverse pitch:
    (a) r.p.m. is controlled by the C.S.U.
    (b) selection should be made with the throttle closed.
    (c) selection places the C.S.U. inoperative.
    (d) is achieved by the blades passing through the feathered position.

Ref. Ch.11. Para.12.4.

23. In the event the propeller overspeeds, constant speed type:
    (a) close the throttle.
    (b) increase overspeed.
    (c) select fully fine.
    (d) increase engine r.p.m.

Ref. Ch.11. Para.12.5.

24. On most large double acting propellers, feathering is accomplished by:
    (a) additional oil pressure provided by the engine-driven booster pump.
    (b) additional oil pressure provided by an electrically driven booster pump.
    (c) assistance from counterweights.
    (d) assistance from the feathering spring.

    Ref. Ch.6. Para.6.2.

25. On most double acting propellers, the feather position will not be achieved unless:
    (a) high boost pressure is selected.
    (b) the engine has stopped.
    (c) the latches are withdrawn.
    (d) the stops are withdrawn.

    Ref. Ch.6. Para.6.2.

26. Within the propeller slipstream, drag will be:
    (a) the same as the drag within the free stream airflow.
    (b) less than the drag in the free stream airflow.
    (c) twice the value of drag in the free stream airflow.
    (d) four times the value of drag in the free stream airflow.

    Ref. Ch.12. Para.12.10.

27. The slipstream effect of a propeller will:
    (a) rotate in the opposite direction as the propeller.
    (b) reduce the effectiveness of the flaps when they are lowered.
    (c) increase the effectiveness of the flaps when they are lowered.
    (d) create a turbulent boundary layer within the slipstream.

    Ref. Ch.12. Para.12.10.

28. On a single engined aircraft, directional stability may be:
    (a) reduced due to the slipstream swirl effect.
    (b) increased by the propeller torque.
    (c) increased by the slipstream swirl effect.
    (d) reduced by the increase of engine r.p.m.

    Ref. Ch.12. Para.12.10.

29. On an aircraft fitted with a left handed propeller and a tail undercarriage, on take-off:
    (a) the nose will not be effected in pitch.
    (b) the nose will pitch down.
    (c) the aircraft will yaw to starboard.
    (d) the nose will pitch up.

    Ref. Ch.12. Para.12.11.

30. A right handed propeller rotates:
    (a) clockwise when viewed from the front.
    (b) clockwise when viewed from the rear.
    (c) anti-clockwise when viewed from the rear.
    (d) to the left when viewed from the cockpit.

    Ref. Ch.12. Para.12.11.

31. With a clockwise rotating propeller, as viewed from the cockpit, the slipstream will:
    (a) rotate anti-clockwise when viewed from the cockpit.
    (b) strike the port side of the fin causing a yaw to port.
    (c) strike the right side of the fin causing a yaw to port.
    (d) strike the left hand side of the fin causing a yaw to starboard.

    Ref. Ch.12. Para.12.12.

32. A propeller is normally more efficient at:
    (a) high speeds and high altitudes.
    (b) low speeds and high altitude.
    (c) low to medium sub-sonic speeds at medium altitudes.
    (d) low to medium speeds at low altitudes.

    Ref. Ch.12. Para.12.14.

33. A low by-pass fan engine has a ratio of:
    (a) 1:1.
    (b) 5:1.
    (c) 15:1.
    (d) 30:1.

    Ref. Ch.12. Para.12.15.

34. A very high by-pass fan engine has a by-pass ratio of:
    (a) 5:1.
    (b) 15:1.
    (c) 30:1.
    (d) 60:1.

Ref. Ch.12. Para.12.15.

35. Reverse thrust in most "Ducted Fan" engines is achieved by:
    (a) exhaust gases aft of the turbines.
    (b) cold reverse thrust from the low pressure compressor.
    (c) cold reverse thrust from the high pressure compressor.
    (d) hot reverse thrust from the low pressure compressor.

Ref. Ch.12. Para.12.15.

36. Advanced Turbo-propellers achieve a by-pass ratio in the order of:
    (a) 5:1.
    (b) 15:1.
    (c) 30:1.
    (d) 60:1.

Ref. Ch.12. Para.12.16.

37. The advanced propeller concept drives the propeller through:
    (a) a gearbox driven from the compressor shaft.
    (b) a gearbox driven from a turbine shaft.
    (c) a gearbox driven from an auxiliary drive.
    (d) an extension of the turbine assembly.

Ref. Ch.12. Para.12.16.

38. The spinner:
    (a) provides a safety lock for the propellers.
    (b) minimises turbulence at the root, or hub, of the propeller.
    (c) minimises turbulence at the tip of the blades.
    (d) reduces the swirl effect of the propeller.

Ref. Ch.12. Para.12.17.

39. A laminated wooden propeller is one which:
    (a) is made from a solid section of wood.
    (b) is made of layers of wood.
    (c) is made of alternate layers of metal and wood.
    (d) is made from plywood layers.

    Ref. Ch.12. Para.12.18.

40. A laminated propeller is:
    (a) bonded together with glue.
    (b) screwed together.
    (c) bolted together.
    (d) made from a single section of wood.

    Ref. Ch.12. Para.12.18.

41. When flight practice of feathering and unfeathering pro-
    pellers is carried out:
    (a) the oil should be allowed to cool before unfeathering is
        carried out.
    (b) maximum boost should be selected before unfeathering.
    (c) the oil must not be allowed to cool too low before
        unfeathering.
    (d) boost must be de-selected before unfeathering.

    Ref. Ch.7. Para.7.10.

42. If the propeller is feathered with the engine stopped on the
    ground:
    (a) the propeller should be unfeathered before the engine
        is started.
    (b) the propeller should be unfeathered manually before
        restarting the engine.
    (c) the propeller should be left in the feathered position
        until the engine is started.
    (d) It will have no effect on the engine start procedure.

    Ref. Ch.7. Para.7.9.

43. When unfeathering a propeller in flight, the throttle should
    be set:
    (a) to max r.p.m.
    (b) to the same r.p.m. as the other engine.
    (c) to minimum r.p.m.

(d) to just above minimum r.p.m.

Ref. Ch.7. Para.7.8.

44. When unfeathering a propeller in flight, the R.P.M. lever must be set:
   (a) to max r.p.m.
   (b) to peak r.p.m.
   (c) just above minimum r.p.m.
   (d) to minimum r.p.m.

Ref. Ch.7. Para.7.8.

45. When unfeathering a propeller in flight, the propeller r.p.m. lever should be moved into the constant speed range:
   (a) before the engine is started.
   (b) after the engine has started.
   (c) after the engine has warmed up.
   (d) before the propeller is unfeathered.

Ref. Ch.7. Para.7.8.

46. When unfeathering a propeller in flight:
   (a) the fuel should be switched on before unfeathering.
   (b) the fuel should be switched on immediately after unfeathering.
   (c) the fuel should be switched on when the engine reaches max r.p.m.
   (d) the fuel should be switched on when peak windmilling speed is reached.

Ref. Ch.7. Para.7.8.

47. When feathering an electric propeller:
   (a) current should be switched off when feathered position is reached.
   (b) current will automatically switch off then feathered position is reached.
   (c) the propeller will feather much quicker than a hydraulic propeller.
   (d) the propeller will feather at about the same speed as a hydraulic propeller.

Ref. Ch.7. Para.7.6.

PROPELLERS

48. Prior to feathering most piston engine propellers:
    (a) the engine must be stationary.
    (b) the throttle must first be fully closed.
    (c) the throttle must be set at flight idle.
    (d) the throttle must be set at ground idle.

    Ref. Ch.7. Para.7.5.

49. When feathering a propeller due to an engine fire:
    (a) operate the fire extinguisher as soon as the fire is detected.
    (b) operate the extinguisher when the engine has been switched off.
    (c) operate the extinguisher when the propeller has stopped.
    (d) operate the extinguisher when ignition has been switched off.

    Ref. Ch.7. Para.7.5.

50. To unfeather a variable pitch propeller:
    (a) move the R.P.M. lever to zero setting.
    (b) push the unfeathering button.
    (c) push the feathering button.
    (d) move the R.P.M. lever to feather.

    Ref. Ch.7. Para.7.4.